# NELLIE BLY

*First Woman Reporter*

# NELLIE BLY

## *First Woman Reporter*

## (1867 — 1922)

*(Seaman)*

## By IRIS NOBLE

D1196386

10197

# JULIAN MESSNER, INC.

## NEW YORK

Published by Julian Messner, Inc.
8 West 40th Street, New York 18

Published simultaneously in Canada
by The Copp Clark Company, Ltd.

© Copyright 1956 by Iris Noble

Library of Congress Catalog Card No. 56-6792

Third Printing, 1957

"To My Mother"

# 1

NOTICE: *Will the gentleman who wrote a letter to the Pittsburgh Dispatch, criticizing our editorial of Friday entitled "What Girls Are Good For," please send his name and address to the editor? Mr. Madden wishes to discuss with the unknown contributor the possibility of his writing a feature article on the same subject for this paper.*

The notice appeared on the inside third page of the *Dispatch,* under the dateline of November 22, 1885. Most readers of the Pittsburgh paper passed it by completely, so small and tucked away was it between a dull article on the Erie Canal and an advertisement for Pears' soap.

One person did read it and to that one, it was as if a miracle had happened.

To Elizabeth Cochrane it was an answer to a prayer. Suppose she hadn't seen it? What if she had neglected, that one day, to open the *Dispatch* and read it?

She was shaking with excitement, standing in the small but elegant hallway of Thomas Kennedy's home. Behind the closed doors of the library she could hear the murmur of voices: her mother's, her older brothers' and her Uncle Thomas' as they sat over their afternoon tea. Those voices had been going on and on for over an hour, now, and the girl knew she was the subject of their discussion. What to do with Elizabeth? She was eighteen years old. Her father, Judge Cochrane, was dead. There was no money to launch her debut into Pittsburgh society, no money to attract suitors for her hand, in fact, she and her mother were living in real poverty, in one housekeeping room, since they had come to Pittsburgh.

Suddenly, in the still, quiet hall, Uncle Thomas' voice came clearly through the closed door. He must have walked nearer, probably to tap out his pipe into the curiously-carved Chinese bowl which he had brought home from his travels. The girl caught a fragment of what he was saying— ". . . why not schoolteaching? . . . or . . . you prefer . . . perhaps companion to old Mrs. Blakely . . . rich . . ."

Elizabeth turned and ran up the stairs. She went into the sitting room, closed the door and crossed hurriedly to the small writing desk, her long black mourning skirt almost tripping her in her haste. Pulling a piece of note paper out of her uncle's fashionably smart writing case, she wrote:

Mr. George A. Madden, Editor of The Pittsburgh *Dispatch*. Dear Sir: In answer to your printed request for the name of the person who answered your editorial "What Girls Are Good For," I am that person and I am most interested in writing articles for your paper. I realize you are not expecting to hear from a woman, but it must have been my ability to write that impressed you. It surely makes no difference whether I am a man or a woman. As I said in my answer to your editorial, girls have the same ability, the same talents and the same intelligence as men. They only lack the same opportunities. I beg of you to give me an interview and—

She flung the pen to the floor. It would not do! If she told him she was a girl he might never answer. If she begged for an interview, he might feel she was appealing to him out of pity or sympathy. It just would not do. On a fresh sheet of note paper she wrote:

Mr. George A. Madden, Editor. Dear Sir: In reply to your request, I am the writer who answered your editorial "What Girls Are Good For." May I suggest next Wednesday afternoon at three o'clock for our appointment? If I do not hear from you to the contrary, I will be at your office at that time. Sincerely, E. Cochrane.

Be a schoolteacher? Or a companion to a rich and cantankerous old woman like Mrs. Blakely? It was not for that her father had taken such pains with her education. She wanted to write. Ever since she was a child she had scribbled all over her schoolbooks—stories, poems, fairy tales. Her father had trained her to think. He had opened up the whole wide world of politics and economics and the law to her. He had even hoped for a while that she might become a lawyer like himself, but when he saw that her bent was for writing, he had encouraged her, taught her to have faith in herself.

There was no use talking to Uncle Thomas or her mother about a writing career. Even if they weren't just amused by the idea, they would point out certain hard, cold, economic facts. To wit, she had no money, she must earn a living. It might take years to write a book.

But it had taken her only one afternoon to write the answer to the editorial. It had impressed George Madden. He was *asking* for articles from her. And it might pay money!

In his cramped and cluttered office that next Wednesday, George Madden sat before his shabby old ink-stained, roll-top desk. His short legs dangled over the floor as he creaked back in his swivel chair, leaned over to jerk a paper off the wall spindle. Papers were everywhere, heaped on his desk and in piles on the floor. Oddly enough, the only clean thing in the room was the cuspidor, it being the office boy's abominated job to clean it three times a day until it shone.

That was not a matter of finickiness, but of necessity. In those days men chewed and spat with great vigor.

Madden was tired and irritable. Beneath his feet, from the floor below, he could feel the vibrations of the presses. He could hear the steady clack-clack of the machines. Usually it was a sound that soothed him. Just hearing it there underneath him was all the sound, the tone, the harmony of the most beautiful of symphonies. His ear was like that of an orchestra conductor's who can hear the slightest flaw in the playing of the farthest man in the farthest row. Madden could come suddenly alert at the tiniest break in the rhythm below.

But today it was not the machines that troubled him. His difficulty lay with the men inside his city room. There they were, his ten reporters, scratching away at long sheets of foolscap with pen and pencil. And when they finished what they were doing, all ten of them would then just sit back and wait for him to tell them what next to cover.

He couldn't understand it. He had known reporters who went searching for news, who had ideas. Was that breed dying out?

From his window he could see the tall buildings of Pittsburgh. It was the Pittsburgh of 1885, a city that in an incredibly short space of time, since the end of the Civil War—and with a good share of its money made out of that war—had shucked off its cow-village frontier ways and emerged into this exciting, corrupt, colorful and inventively progressive manufacturing city, making news faster than he could print it.

The city he could cope with—if he had the men to do it.

His staff was made up of hard-working, competent newspapermen. But on a day like this he felt he would like to take all of their ten heads and knock them together just to see if just one spark of imagination might not be jolted out of them.

"I don't get what you're driving at, Mr. Madden." Pelton, his lean tall assistant, who seemed to exude ink vapor and pencil dust and machine oil from his pores instead of the more human variety of perspiration, leaned over the desk and jabbed a bluish finger at a page of copy. One arm garter slid down over the elbow of his black alpaca shirt, and he pushed it up with a gesture of long habit. "What's wrong with that story? It's the Triangle Merchants' Dinner. Jones covered it. He got all the names straight. He got some of the main speech. What more do you want?"

"It's only one story. What about other stories?" Madden spoke in short, sharp barks of exasperation. "This story was in the banquet room. What about what happened in the lobby? In the bar? Fifty of the biggest financiers in the country there and Jay Gould their guest—there should be fifty stories. What's old Gould up to? What did Andrew Carnegie say to him? What mergers are coming up? What firms are due to collapse? Why, I could have picked up enough material there to fill the whole paper!"

"But you told him just to—"

"I know! I know! But can't he use his brains? Doesn't he have any curiosity? Pelton, the *Dispatch* is going stale. *Something* has to be done."

Now the assistant editor was thoroughly alarmed. He knew Madden to be a hardheaded, conservative man ordinarily. But when he reached these moments of despair over the paper, when he decided the *Dispatch* needed gingering up, then he seemed to lose all caution. He was apt to do queer and startling things. And before matters got back to normal there would be trouble, and he, Pelton, would be in as much hot water as his boss.

The door opened. A boy's tight red curls peeped around the doorframe. A freckled face showed a mixture of fear and excitement. "A lady to see you, sir."

"Not in."

"But she says she has an appointment for three o'clock. And she's right here in the city room and the men are gawking at her." The boy thrust a letter at Pelton and scuttled out.

Madden took the letter and glanced at it. It was his,

[ 12 ]

all right, confirming an appointment with E. Cochrane. But what was a woman doing here?

He thought back. Pelton had written an editorial on "What Girls Are Good For." It was the usual thing. Girls belonged in the home; it was to be deplored that some of them were venturing out to get jobs. It encouraged them to think they should vote or own property, this business of leaving home, and some of them might so far forget their noble womanhood as to join with the detested women suffragists who were undermining the whole fabric of society.

An answer had come in the mail from this Cochrane. It was a blistering answer. It said that girls had brains and ability and were good for something else besides cooking and homework and sewing fringe all over antimacassars. Said that the country needed all the talents it could get, but by its treatment of girls it was robbing itself of half the brains, half the skills, of its citizens. It was a letter that rang with passionate sincerity, calling for women to take their rightful place alongside of men in what was now a man's world.

It was well written. It would have been good, readable copy for any newspaper.

Well, maybe Cochrane couldn't come and had sent this woman with a message. "Send her in, Pelton," he said wearily.

When Elizabeth walked into that room and stood facing the editor at his desk, neither she nor Madden could have had the slightest idea of how momentous was this first meeting. Neither could foresee a future for this girl that would mean both fame and notoriety, high honors and scandalous attacks. They could not see that from this room she would walk into paths no woman had walked before, paths that would take her into the homes of the great and the rich, into the slums of the poor, into insane asylums and pesthouses, across oceans and into foreign lands. Neither could hear, far off in the future, the screaming, cheering applauding crowds—Americans and people in strange, foreign costumes, too—that would take her to their hearts, trampling each other to get a look at her or touch her hand.

Madden saw only a very feminine, timid girl in mourning clothes. She was a small girl and in her slender face her large gray eyes seemed enormous and somehow compelling. And she was very young, barely eighteen, he guessed.

She didn't wait for him to speak.

"I know you were expecting to see a man, Mr. Madden. But I am E. Cochrane—Elizabeth Cochrane. I was afraid if you knew I was a woman you wouldn't want to see me. And I very much want the chance to write for your newspaper. You mentioned my doing an article for you?"

He stared at her, astounded. Women didn't write for newspapers. Everyone knew that.

"Sit down, miss." As she moved to the chair he noticed again how young she was. She must have only just begun to put up her red-brown hair, because it was amateurishly pinned and threatening to come tumbling down around her shoulders at any minute. Her small bonnet was slipping sidewise. Her black dress of mourning was a pathetic, touching compromise between the hourglass silhouette of the older woman and the shapeless frock of the child. The bustle at the back was a flat, pancake affair and it wobbled when she walked, for she was too slim to support it well. Her black, shiny high-button shoes were neat on her very small feet.

"I'm sorry you made the trip down here, Miss Cochrane. Because I'll have to disappoint you. I couldn't possibly—"

"Please! Before you say that, please listen to me. I *can* write. I could be a good newspaper reporter."

"Now don't talk nonsense. You're too young. Even if you weren't, I don't employ women." But his curiosity got the better of him. "I just don't understand, Miss Cochrane, why you should want to do this. Do you have some idea that writing for newspapers is a romantic fling?"

"Of course not." She sat forward on the edge of her seat, gripping her purse tightly. "I know it is hard work. But I must earn a living. My mother and I are penniless. My two brothers are just beginning in business here; I can't be a burden on them. And the only thing I do well is write. I've *proved* that to you. My father was a lawyer and when he had cases to try he used to send me out— he used to say I was scouting his cases—and I would get all the facts, all kinds of hidden information from families and neighbors, information that might not come out in a courtroom. Then I would write up a report. That kind of training—it isn't much different from newspaper reporting, is it?"

"I thought you said you wanted to do one article." The editor sounded dazed. "Now you're talking about newspaper *reporting*—you really mean that you want to be a *reporter*? Whew! Now I think I've heard everything!"

To his own dumfounded astonishment, he found himself becoming interested. She talked well. In spite of her demure manner, she talked with poise and maturity and she used words as if they were good tools to express herself with.

"One article alone won't feed me. If I can prove to you that you will want to print what I write, then let me write more. I can do it as well as anyone on your paper." Elizabeth was not boasting. It was a statement of fact. "And I have ideas."

"What kind of ideas?"

Her face lit up, intense, earnest. "Mr. Madden, I've been all over Pittsburgh, looking at everything. One day I walked down to the slums. Sir, there are a million stories there! Let me go and find them, not just in the slums—everywhere. I found two children that day, just babies, sleeping in a doorway. I learned they had no parents, no one to take care of them, except for the kindness of neighbors who fed them in turns. The older one was nine years old and she looked after her brother. Isn't that a story? I think people want to read about themselves. Your subscribers are working people mostly. They don't want to read just what some woman in society is doing, or what some big politician is saying, or what is happening in Washington or Wall Street. They want to read about their own lives—how they work and live and the kind of houses they have—and what they *think!*"

Madden stared at her. Ten minutes ago he had been wondering if there was such a thing as a fresh idea, and if there was, where would he find the person who could put it on paper. Here she was—a reporter who would go out and mingle with people and *find* stories. He had dreamed of this.

He tried to be cautious. He explained to her: a newspaper was supposed to report about big people, not little ones. People bought the *Dispatch* to read about the rich, the famous, the influential.

"I'm not denying that, Mr. Madden. But isn't there room for both kinds of stories?"

He threw caution away. He wanted to know more of her ideas.

And Elizabeth Cochrane literally poured them out, leaving him bewildered at the profusion, the variety, the daring of them. She would take a photographer with her and explore a factory. She would go into shops and talk to the women who worked there; she would go home with them and find out how they lived, where they learned their trades, what they did for amusement. She had seen children of ten working in the mills from dawn to dusk. How many Pittsburgh citizens gave them even a thought? And she would go to the orphan asylums, the poorhouses, hospitals, prisons—she would go everywhere!

As she spoke, he was amazed at what was happening right in front of his eyes.

Again and again her personality changed in swift flashes of characterization. Why, Madden thought, this youngster is an actress! In rapid succession he saw her turn into a tired woman coming home from work. He saw her old and poor and hobbled with rheumatism, as she spoke of the poorhouse. He saw her face flood with tenderness and become almost matronly as she spoke of the children. She was restless as she talked. She paced up and down. But he felt, too, that she was totally un-aware of the fact that she was acting out her thoughts.

He slapped the desk with the flat of his hand. He would have given that hand—and arm, too—to have had a man on his staff to whom he could have turned over her ideas. But there wasn't any.

They were *her* ideas. She had a right to her chance.

George A. Madden did the most revolutionary thing in his life. "All right," he said. "We'll see about this. I think you are on the right track. I want you to do a fea-ture for me—no, you pick your own topic. If it's any good, then you'll be a reporter for me. I mean it—" he waved her grateful stammerings aside. "Don't thank me. Do a good feature and you've got a job. At least"—caution returning—"I'll give you a chance with some of your ideas."

The article on divorce reached him two days later. It was well written, excitingly written. The controversy over divorce—over whether people should or should not have the right to divorce—had been fought over in pulpits and senates and law courts for many years. The subject had been chewed over in articles until it was limp as a rag. But she had managed to give it freshness. Elizabeth remembered all the painstaking legal work her father had done on the subject; she added social, humanistic argu-ments to advocate that people should have the right to free themselves from intolerable relationships.

Madden liked it. It was vivid and bright and easy reading.

He sent her a note: she had fulfilled her share of the bargain. Now she would have her assignment as a re-porter. She was to visit a factory that bottled jams and jellies and pickles and other condiments—the Grubacher Company. A photographer would meet her in front of the factory at ten o'clock Monday morning.

So far Elizabeth had kept what she was doing a secret from her family. The article on divorce would be in the Sunday paper. Let it speak for itself, break the news, then she could take it from there.

Sunday came. As usual, the Cochranes visited the Kennedys for Sunday noon dinner. All morning, untouched, the *Dispatch* lay on the hall table. It was not proper to open it until after church services. Even then Elizabeth controlled her eagerness. She didn't dare touch it; she was too agitated. She wanted her mother and the others to read it first.

But after dinner Uncle Thomas leafed through the pages without a comment. Her brothers went through it carefully, in turn, discussing the local news with each other. Her mother glanced at the headlines.

Elizabeth could hardly contain herself. Wasn't it printed? Had Mr. Madden changed his mind? She couldn't stand it any longer. She grabbed the paper and went through it, item by item.

There it was! The top article—prominently displayed on the feature section. Bold, black type slashed the title "Divorce" at the head of the column. But it was signed—Nellie Bly—not Elizabeth Cochrane.

It was the fashion of those days for pen names. Also, Madden had made inquiries and found that Elizabeth's father had been Judge Cochrane, member of an old, influential Pennsylvania family. The town where Elizabeth was born was called Cochran's Mills after the family. It would not do to bandy around such a name signed after articles on divorce.

An office boy happened to be passing, whistling a tune. It was Stephen Foster's popular song "Nellie Bly." It struck Madden as a good pen name, catchy and also one that *Dispatch* readers were familiar with.

And thus she was to gain a new name—Nellie Bly.

When she disclosed her authorship, the storm in the family was what she had expected. Women did not cheapen themselves by appearing in print, certainly no woman of the Cochrane-Kennedy family. Uncle Thomas was outraged. Her brothers were furious. Her mother was wronged and aggrieved. This was no work for a gently reared, cultured young girl. They would not permit it; how could she have done such a thing without consulting them? She would be associating with riffraff, she might be sent into saloons! Uncle Thomas roared.

Elizabeth thought it best not to mention Monday or the bottle factory.

But she faced them with her mind made up. She must earn a living, she pointed out to them. She refused to be a companion or a governess—these were only polite names for being a high-class servant. And she was being paid five dollars for this article.

In 1885 this was no small sum for two days' work. Even Uncle Thomas was impressed. But what finally defeated both her uncle and her brothers was not the money, but Elizabeth's determination and—to everyone's surprise—her mother's sudden about-face. Mrs. Cochrane had her own doubts about the suitability of this new work, but she wasn't going to stand by and hear the menfolk bully her daughter.

"You know very well," she scolded them, with a twinkle of humor on her plump face, "that you are all secretly afraid you will have Elizabeth on your hands and have to support her. So don't stand in her way when she wants to be independent."

That Monday morning at the corner of Howell and Jane streets, in the heart of the slum-factory area, Elizabeth met the photographer from the *Dispatch*. He was a tall man, bald and dyspeptic, his hands full of his big black camera, his tripod, his plates and flash powder. His name was Sam, he told her. And that's all he did say. He was there to take pictures. If Madden wanted to send a woman or a hippopotamus along, that was Madden's affair.

His matter-of-factness was just what Elizabeth needed. It was obvious that he was looking to her to take the lead. She could not show him that she was scared, that this was her first job.

Getting into the factory was easy. The factory manager was pleased. He had visions of good publicity for his plant. He took them on a quick tour and then back to his office, just off the big room where the women stood in long rows to wash the bottles. He was charmed with Elizabeth, delighted with her innocent little questions and her girlish curiosity. He told her of course she could wander around in the room and talk to the women if she wanted to. It was a waste of her time but it would give her something to do while the photographer took pictures of himself and his handsome new office.

Sam took endless pictures. There were no plates in the camera, but the manager didn't know that. He was exhausted by posing when Elizabeth came back. He teased

[ 21 ]

her playfully, fatherly, for her curiosity. What in the world had she been doing all that time?

He found out—when the story broke.

Again it was signed Nellie Bly, and it told of all the things she had learned from the women themselves . . . the long working hours, the terrible conditions of cold and damp and of standing for hours on tired, aching feet; of the bottles that broke and cut the girls' hands to ribbons in long, ugly slashes; of the water that splashed, hot and steaming, over hands and faces at the washing sinks. It told of complaints that the manager ignored: the dirty, unsanitary conditions; the rats that came crawling around for scraps of food fallen on the floor; the one toilet for both men and women on two whole floors of the factory.

There were no pictures of the potbellied little manager. Instead, displayed in three columns across the second page were pictures of girls at work, pictures of girls with their feet bundled in rags against the bitter cold of the cement floor.

The story was written in a highly personal, highly emotional vein. Nellie Bly was furiously indignant. Every line was a trumpet call for justice.

The reaction of Pittsburgh citizens was a mixed one. The *Dispatch* was a sold-out issue. Subscriptions jumped. The working people dug down into worn-out wallets and pocketbooks to take the paper, because this was their story and Nellie was their champion.

On the other side the story was no less a sensation, though there it stirred a tempest of anger and pious condemnation. Factory owners, whose plants were no better than Grubacher's, were enraged and denounced Nellie,

Madden and the *Dispatch* for their presumption in daring to criticize their way of doing business. They called Nellie radical and blasted Madden as irresponsible. Some clergymen preached sermons branding Nellie an immoral woman who pried into matters wordly instead of sticking to matters spiritual as befitted a woman. Civic groups sent a delegation to the *Dispatch* with orders the paper was to boost Pittsburgh, not expose it.

But who was Nellie Bly? And what was a woman doing writing articles for newspapers, anyway!

Madden was pleased. The *Dispatch* was being read, that was the main thing. He laughed at Pelton for his warnings of trouble to come.

He gave Elizabeth another assignment. This time she would have a free hand and she could go anywhere she wanted, write any kind of a story, and she could have a staff artist to go with her to sketch illustrations for her.

So Elizabeth Cochrane, eighteen years old, went into the slums of Pittsburgh. She walked through narrow, dirty, garbage-strewn streets. She talked to women and to men. She found conditions more horrible than anything she had dreamed of—whole families living in one room without heat to warm them or enough food to feed them—tenements that were fire traps—tenements that were rat ridden. Here were children who had never been to school, and other children of ten and twelve who were sent to work in the mills because otherwise there wouldn't be enough food for the family.

These children struck horror to her heart. They were tiny little old men and women, their minds empty of any natural childish thought, their bodies already stunted and twisted by work too heavy and hours too long.

She saw hunger. She saw fear. She listened to angry talk about the rich who cared nothing for the poor, and she sought out men who belonged to the Knights of Labor and who were agitating for an eight-hour day. But mostly she talked to women, following them to the mills and shops to see where and how they worked.

The "Nellie Bly" articles became a regular feature of the *Dispatch*. And month by month the pressure mounted against Madden to stop her. Factory owners, landlords, big businessmen, all concentrated their fire against one newspaper and against one "meddling" female.

Madden wavered. True, he had received warm support from many reform leaders and from woman-suffrage and trade-union leaders, from educators and from some preachers. But they were not the people who could place or pull out advertisements in his newspaper. So he compromised.

"We'll give them a breathing space, Nellie—do you mind my calling you that? I always think of you as Nellie. Now we'll stop the stories for a while. In the meantime, I want you to try your hand at something else."

"The "something else" was a theater opening of the new play *Dr. Jekyll and Mr. Hyde*, starring Mr. Mansfield. Like a good reporter, Elizabeth was eager to try every kind of newspaper work. She went to her new assignment with almost as much enthusiasm as she had for her special stories. She even bought fashionable new clothes. Uncle Thomas was proud to be her escort. He had agreed to it with some doubts—what was she going to do at a theater opening? To his delight she sat quietly,

an attractive, well-dressed girl, watching the performance and making notes on her program. He found it very
satisfying, too, that she asked him for help; he knew who
was who of Pittsburgh society who sat in the expensive
boxes and he knew a great deal of the stage itself.

Through the months of January and February and
on through the spring and summer of 1886, Elizabeth
covered the theater, the opera, concerts, lectures, art
exhibits. She enjoyed it. But she was marking time, waiting for Madden to give her back the kind of assignments
she wanted to do.

She begged him to let her go back to the slums.

Finally he gave in. She could do a factory story. But
first he had another story for her, one that he was sure
she would like. He wanted her to visit the new Western
Penitentiary, the most modern and advanced of its kind.
Then she'd be free to do her own story.

Two assignments—and both to her liking. Elizabeth
was excited and happy. She visited the new prison and
talked to the warden. He was most co-operative. He took
her around and showed her the advances he had made:
the clean quarters, the reading rooms, the shops where
the men could be taught a trade. There would be no
more whippings here, no more starving the men into
submission. In the account she wrote for the *Dispatch*
she minced no words in telling the horrible stories of
what happened to most prisoners in other jails of that
time.

Then she went to the factory.

She knew just which one she wanted. One day, happening to pass by a big, dilapidated brick building in the
heart of the slums, she had been fascinated by a glimpse

she had caught of the basement workroom. More than a hundred women seemed to be crouching there over long tables, although she couldn't tell what they were doing. This was the place to which she took the artist who would make sketches for her.

Elizabeth tried first to get into the main factory upstairs. The gatekeeper had his orders; no visitors.

All morning she waited outside in an agony of indecision. How was she going to get into that basement? Then, just before noon, the women poured up and out into the street—from a door she hadn't seen. And as they came into the bright sunlight every single one of them did the same thing! They put up their hands to shield their eyes, rubbed their eyes as if the light were too painful to bear.

The artist made a quick, rapid sketch. It made a superb picture.

Now it was her turn. She walked over to one of the women, debating in her mind what to say and how to get in.

The woman spoke first, unwittingly giving Elizabeth her opportunity. "You lookin' for work, honey? If you want a job you couldn't a come at a better time. They said they was planning on hiring some girls tomorrow. You come back with us after lunch and I'll bet you get in."

She went back with them. The foreman looked at her sourly, at her soft white, well-cared-for hands.

"You don't look to me like you've ever worked before. If you want a job you might as well know you are going to work hard. We don't go for any pampering. Any complaints and you just pick yourself up and get out!" He rounded this out with a few choice curses on the troubles he had with beginners.

He led her to a bench. Long strands of copper wire were placed in front of her. The foreman grabbed them in one hand, looped a cord around them, flipped a cord end inside the loop and pulled it tight. "See? Just keep doing this every two inches all the way down the cable. No—not like that! Clumsy! Do it like I showed you!"

For ten minutes he stood over her. And for ten minutes he showered curses and abuse on her head. Her fingers ached with the tension of trying to do it right and fast, and with the strain of pulling the heavy cord. Across from her and on all sides women's hands were flying, doing the same operation as she was, over and over. Thick callouses on thumbs and finger joints showed where the heavy cords had thickened the skin. Her own unprotected hands were soon sore and raw.

Now she understood, too, the reason why the women had shielded their eyes against the sun. There was hardly any light in the room. Gas jets along walls gave a flickering, yellowish glow, but they were of little help over the tables. In order to see their work the women bent so low over the tables that back and shoulder muscles were tortured with pain.

The foreman was called away. This gave her some moments to talk to her fellow workers. In answer to her questions, they whispered about their splitting headaches, of their fear of going blind over their work. Their hands were scored and roughened by the cables, their backs in constant pain. No matter how fast they worked the foreman was standing over them, urging them, yelling at them in the foulest of language to go faster. The speed was inhuman.

At the end of an hour Elizabeth was fired.

Being thirsty, she had left her bench and had found an old sink in one corner of the room. She was rinsing out the one dirty glass when the foreman spotted her.

"What are you doing here?" he roared. "Get back to your bench. You ask permission if you want to leave it, for anything, you hear?"

Her temper exploded. "I don't ask anyone's permission to get a drink of water!"

She was fired.

The next day her story appeared. This time there was a new quality in it. It was no longer an I-saw story. It was an I-was-there, a personal experience story burning with the deepest sense of outrage and insult. Reading it, people felt that they, too, had lived through that day with her, that their hands hurt and their backs ached, that their eyes were tortured. It was the best reporting she had ever done.

The article she had written on the prison had come out the day before—and now this one. It was too much.

The attack, slanderous and vile, centered around her prison story. She was called an abandoned, evil woman to have walked through a prison full of nothing but men, looked into their cells, talked to them. Shameless! City officials denounced her as incompetent to judge their prison systems. A rival newspaper printed an editorial demanding all decent women shun such a one as Nellie Bly, who could so lower the standards of female decency as to write about the coarse subject of the life of men in jail.

The outcry did not lessen with the passing of days. On the contrary, it grew. Her account of the basement factory infuriated many businessmen. They sent Madden an ultimatum: no more stories like that or they would boycott the *Dispatch*, pull out their advertisements. There were many voices that praised both the stories. But these were quiet voices, not the loud ones or the ones with money and authority.

Madden capitulated.

Elizabeth was assigned back to reporting the theater, back to the art reviews, back to the respectable job of covering lectures and recitals. He raised her salary to fifteen dollars a week, an excellent salary for a young girl in those times.

2

Several months went by, quiet, uneventful months. Now it was October, 1886. Elizabeth had gained for herself a secure position with the *Dispatch*, covering the whole field of drama and the arts, and Madden was pleased. Her reviews, unsigned, were a regular feature of the newspaper, both daily and Sunday. Pittsburgh readers found them lively and discriminating, often possessing flashes of humor. They lacked the sharp wit to make them really outstanding, and they also lacked something in profound scholarship. But they were far above average and the editor was satisfied.

Her family was proud of her. Reviews of opera and stage were considered "literary" accomplishments . . . a far cry from seeing Elizabeth's pen name coupled with factory girls and basement shops, slums and prisons. From her own co-workers, the newspapermen of the city, she received an honor never dreamed of before for a woman; she was invited to join the newly formed Pittsburgh Press Club.

Consequently, both her family and George Madden were amazed when she suddenly announced that she was taking leave of the paper for a six-month vacation in Mexico. True, none of them had ever really expected that her enthusiasm for newspaper work was anything but a brief fire which would quickly die out. But Madden had not expected it to happen so soon.

Mrs. Cochrane agreed to go along. And in the midst of packing and planning and fittings at the seamstress' and finally boarding the train, Elizabeth's mother dreamed her own dreams and thought her own thoughts. She looked at her daughter seated across from her in the railway coach, and marveling at the change one year had made in her. Elizabeth was dressed well. In a dark blue, light wool traveling costume, her slight figure was beginning to mature. The tight-fitting jacket buttoned down the front to a point over her flat stomach, revealed a nice figure—even though not quite as rounded as the fashion of those days demanded.

It was time for her daughter to be considering marriage. The mysterious disappearance of the family fortunes at the death of Judge Cochrane had left his wife too bewildered to plan carefully for Elizabeth's future. But she had never really worried. Both the Cochranes and the Kennedys had names to be reckoned with and an entree into the homes of the old, proud, established families—here in Pittsburgh and elsewhere. On her father's side Elizabeth was descended from Lord Cochrane, the famous English admiral. Her great-grandfather Cochrane was one of a number of men who had written a declaration of independence in Maryland long before Jefferson had penned his. On her mother's side, her great-grandfather had been a man of enormous wealth, at one time owning almost all of Somerset County in Pennsylvania. His wife had been an English noblewoman's daughter. They had eloped and fled to America to escape the wrath of her father. Here this ancestor and both his sons had been officers in the Revolutionary War. Afterward he was sheriff of Somerset County—a title of great honor and respect but with very few duties.

With this background, even without money, Mrs. Cochrane could take her place in Pittsburgh society. Her sons were beginning to make a go of their rubber factory. They had friends. Uncle Thomas had friends. And these friends had sons or brothers who were eligible bachelors for Elizabeth to marry.

"What are you smiling about?" Elizabeth asked her suddenly.

The question caught Mrs. Cochrane unprepared. She jumped, guiltily. "Oh," she said hastily, "I was just thinking, dear, how much your looks have improved. I do like the way you are wearing your hair in that soft bang. You have a natural curl and it is most becoming."

The girl looked at herself indifferently, trying to catch a glimpse of herself in the railway coach window. "I wish they would go back to ringlets, instead of piling it all on top of one's head. I have the Cochrane ears, all right. Long, pointed ears. I always feel like the grandmother in 'Little Red Riding Hood—the better to hear you with, my dear.' It's a good thing," she went on, talking about herself as if she were a stranger, "that I have nice eyes. Otherwise I'd be terribly plain."

She did have nice eyes. Large and gray, they were startlingly expressive. When she was animated they actually glowed; when she was quiet they were hauntingly mournful.

[ 32 ]

Mrs. Cochrane launched her campaign. "It's really time you were married, Elizabeth. You don't want to be a spinster, do you? Isn't there anyone you have met that you care for?"

"No. And I don't want to get married. Not yet."

"But why not?"

"Because once you're married, that's the end of it. I couldn't write—I couldn't run off to Mexico like this—I couldn't do any thing I *wanted* to do, just what some man *told* me to do. Mamma, I see a gleam of match-making in your eye. Are you planning to palm me off on some Mexican señor?"

Mrs. Cochrane could only wish that her daughter's sense of humor didn't always crop up to switch the subject whenever it was something the mother thought important. Elizabeth was solemn enough about her own projects, goodness knows—and stubborn! When she was a tiny child she had been given a pink dress. She had loved that dress so much, insisted on wearing it so much, that the family began calling her "Pinky." Even now they sometimes used it as a nickname. Yes, she was stubborn, this daughter of hers, and courageous, much too sure of herself and made so too quickly. Unpredictable, strongly passionate in her feelings, she was contemptuous of weakness in others but blind to her own. Mrs. Cochrane knew her well and was worried. Where were these strange qualities to lead this child of hers?

If Madden had been there, he could have added his own private worries. He sensed in Elizabeth a contradiction. In her work she embraced the problems of the whole of mankind—and womankind; in her personal life she had not one friend, not one real human relationship that she had voluntarily made.

They arrived in Mexico, and suddenly every day was filled with adventure. They wandered—by coach, by wagon, by burro—into little towns and big ones. Villagers, who had never seen such a sight as two unescorted, unchaperoned women walking their mud streets, asking questions, poking their noses into homes and churches and jails, stared at them as if they were devils. Extreme poverty had driven desperate men into becoming bandits; some of whom, like Robin Hood, robbed the rich to give to the poor or else organized bands to resist the tax collectors of a bad government. It was dangerous for gringo women to be traveling in those times; they were threatened with capture for ransom money, and it was no idle threat. Mexico was in the upheaval of revolutionary days and foreigners were apt to get caught in the middle.

But Elizabeth was not only on vacation, she was looking for stories to send back to the *Dispatch* and nothing could stop her. She kept her eyes open. She asked questions. She forced her way into jails, into hospitals—everywhere, paying no attention to scares or threats. Poverty here, she found, was worse than anything she had seen in the United States. Whole families slept in the streets of Mexico City and Vera Cruz, homeless and penniless, the sick with the well. Superstition, not education, was taught the people.

She was caught in the grip of a nervous tension that would not let her be still. It showed in the quick way she walked, in the way she paced the floor at night, to her mother's alarm, in a perpetual little frown between her eyes, a fixed tightness of her mouth.

This tension had little to do with Mexico. It came from an inner conflict.

Her decision to take this kind of a vacation had not been for the reasons Madden suspected or the kind her mother hoped for. This was an important moment in her life and she had fateful decisions to make. So much had happened in the past year that she needed time to think and test herself.

Had her job with the *Dispatch* merely been the result of one of those rare combinations of luck, of being the right person in the right place at the right time? Was she a reporter or a pet whim of Madden's? Could she stand alone without him? This was why she wanted to test her own wings in a strange country. Above all, did she have the courage and the strength to leave the *Dispatch*, where she had security and reputation and a pay check that was almost on a par with those of men reporters?

She wrote from Vera Cruz, where she was the only female passenger on the mule-drawn streetcar and where the men looked at her with disgust: "But I defied the gaze of the passengers and showed them that a free American girl can accommodate herself to the circumstances without the aid of a man."

Madden printed it, but it sounded to him like a child sticking out her tongue at grownups.

But it was more than that. She was working out a standard for herself. A free American girl could go anywhere without the aid of a man. Elizabeth Cochrane, therefore, could go on without the aid of George A. Madden. Though she was not quite able yet to face it, she was getting ready to leave the *Dispatch*.

Suddenly, without warning, her energy was gone. She was exhausted. One morning she could not get out of bed. Mrs. Cochrane called a doctor to see her, in the small hotel room in Vera Cruz. Her mother was really worried and she questioned the doctor closely. Could Elizabeth have caught some disease while she was visiting the hospitals or in the slum homes?

The doctor shook his head. Since he spoke only Spanish they could only gather from his gestures that there was nothing physically wrong with Elizabeth.

"We'll rest here a few days, child." Her mother decided, her capable hands smoothing the rough pillow, adjusting the feather bed so that the girl would be more comfortable. "You've been doing entirely too much running around. Women were not meant to be so active."

Now, for once, the powerful forces that drove Elizabeth were quiet. She was forced to think, not to do. Her mind slowly went back over the past year.

For a while she had been a storm center. She had been heaped with praise, spun into notoriety, looked upon with awe. Two days ago a letter from Madden said that the sponsors of a bill in the state legislature to limit the working hours of children from ten to eight a day had used her name and stories to support their case.

She had also heard the name of Nellie Bly spoken of with fury and scorn. She had been hurt by the attacks against her, by the names she had been called. But she had been hurt only superficially by them. She could shrug them off.

The real hurt had come from the man she respected

[ 36 ]

and admired. George A. Madden had stopped her from doing the kind of stories that were important, her own stories. For a little while he had dared to do something brave and unconventional, but he could not stand up for long against the weight of public opinion and the money waved under his nose by his advertisers. He had stopped her from following her own ideas. He had pulled her out of the center of the whirlpool and into a quiet backwash that would offend no one.

That he had kept her on his staff at all was more than most other newspaper editors would have done. She admitted that much. But was she to go on writing polite little stories announcing the newest lecture by Mark Twain, the latest renditions of the Pittsburgh Choral Society?

That she would go on, she never doubted. In this both her mother and Madden had been wrong. But where was she going? And why *must* she go on? She couldn't answer that; she only knew she must. There was in her such a tremendous desire for personal achievement that she couldn't stop. The odds against her were a million to one, almost. Only a handful of women had ever achieved professional recognition in the America of that century—or in any country for the past *several* centuries, for that matter.

Although she had teased her mother and pretended not to listen when she spoke of marriage, actually Elizabeth had heard every word. She knew all the arguments for getting married and being settled down, but they just had no meaning for her. Her dreams of romance were vague and cloudy and tucked away in the back of her mind where they couldn't interfere with what she wanted to do first.

Judge Cochrane had taught her to think for herself and act *beyond* herself. He had taken her behind the scenes of his courtroom to see and understand human problems, the suffering and the tragedies, even the comic side that underlaid every case of plaintiff versus defendant. Her childhood had been unorthodox, challenging, free. From her mother she had learned stubbornness and persistence and the ability to pretend to meekness if it would get her her own way.

She was not like other girls.

Elizabeth lay quietly on the rude, narrow bed that was the best the hotel could offer. Violet shadows under her eyes spoke of her sleepless nights and looked out of place on her fresh, young face; the frown on her forehead came and went. The room was airless; doctors disapproved of fresh air for sick people.

If it was just for the money to support herself and her mother, then the *Dispatch* was as good as any paper. If she wanted just to be a reporter, she had a secure niche in Pittsburgh. But that wasn't all she wanted!

At first she had been led only by curiosity to go out and see what went on in the lives of other people. But once she had written the stories she found herself with a responsibility. *"Help us, Nellie Bly!"*—people begged her in their letters. The folk she had met in the slums, the working folk, were poor and they led lives of shocking deprivation that sometimes led to acts of cruelty, stupidity, often even of vice. But she had met there a strength she had found nowhere else. Families clung together; neighbors helped each other; people shared what little they had with someone even less fortunate. She had seen there real love for one's fellow man. And always they struggled—to make a better world for themselves and particularly for their children.

She could not desert them. Deserting them meant also a belittling of herself and her own ambitions.

One day Mrs. Cochrane returned from shopping to find her dressed and up and standing at the window.

"Pinky! What are you doing? You get right back into bed this min—"

She stopped, amazed. The face her daughter turned to her had lost all of its tension, all of the listlessness of the last few days. It was alive and radiant, healthy and intense.

"I'm fine. I never felt better." Elizabeth ran the palms of her hands in a quick, glad motion up the sides of her cheeks. She tugged at her hair, pulling it loose. "Mother, I've made up my mind. It's no use your talking to me about marriage—not yet. I want to go on writing for newspapers. But not in Pittsburgh. I'm going to New York."

Mrs. Cochrane started to protest. "But why New York?"

"Why? Because New York has the biggest papers, the greatest papers, in the whole country. And if the papers are big, then the men who run them must be big, too. There's Mr. Dana of the *Sun* and Mr. Pulitzer, publisher of the *World*. There's the *Times*— surely the men who run these papers are big enough and bold enough to take a chance with me. It's not as if I weren't already known to them. I have a reputation. And I know I can succeed there. I can sell them—"

"But why not stay in Pittsburgh, with the *Dispatch*?" Her mother had the sensation of futility, as if she were reaching for Elizabeth and the girl had already passed her by, tearing off into life.

"Because Madden won't let me write what I want to write. And it just came to me what it is I have to offer newspapers that they just *can't* turn down . . . because it's never been done before. Remember the story of the basement shop—where I actually went in and worked? That's the answer. That's what is so special. I'll go to New York and I'll work in the shops or the factories; I'll pretend to be sick so I can go to the hospital—not as an interviewer where people tell you just what they want you to believe, but where I can see for myself. And then I'll write the story and it will be a story I've really lived through."

"You aren't going to live in a tenement!"

"I might—for a week or two." She laughed exuberantly, in pure triumph and confidence in herself.

"But I still don't see why."

"Mamma, you couldn't spend one whole day in those slums without wanting to do something to—to wipe them out—to help people like that who are robbed and overworked and underpaid, who are sick and helpless and miserable."

Mrs. Cochrane looked at her daughter with a long, searching look. To her mind came the stories the Judge used to read to them in the evenings of the Knights of the Round Table who went out into distant lands, into dangerous forests and into murky swamps—armed only with their slender spears and their dauntless faith to fight for justice and right. They were crusaders. It came

[ 40 ]

to Mrs. Cochrane that her daughter, her small, jaunty little daughter, was a crusader, too. The sage-green traveling costume was not shining armor and her pencil was hardly a spear, but just the same that is what she was—a crusader.

The Judge had been like that. As his wife she had encouraged him, stood by him. Could she do less for their daughter?

She took a long breath.

"In that case"—she stood up, her plump shoulders straightening in a determined manner—"in that case, I think we had just better forget about the rest of Mexico and get back to Pittsburgh as fast as we can. There's a lot to be done. You'll have to work for a while to save the money. You'll need a whole new wardrobe, but I can sew most of that myself. Not all of it," she broke off, managing a smile that gave her face the sturdy, wholesome sweetness of her own famous apple dumplings. "I'll want you to have some really stylish things. I'm not going to let you be ashamed in front of those puffed-up New Yorkers." She paused. "There's just one thing, Elizabeth. I know you very well. I don't question how much you care about those 'poor people' of yours, but I wonder just how much of this wanting to go to New York isn't to satisfy your own ambitions, too. Don't fly so high you can't come down again."

Mother and daughter faced each other for a long moment. Then they smiled in complete understanding.

"And your name won't be Elizabeth Cochrane any more," she added softly. "It will be Nellie Bly."

It would be Nellie Bly—except for the brief years of her marriage—for the rest of her life.

[ 41 ]

# 3

By the summer of 1887 Nellie Bly was in New York, and the first three months were the worst of her life.

It was hot, the hottest summer the city had known. Every day brought new accounts of people sickening and dying of the terrible, stifling heat. Work must go on; somehow people dragged themselves out of their homes in the mornings, hurried into the slight protection of the buildings, where they worked, sat sweltering until it was time to go home, drooping, panting, perspiring in the horse trolleys or slowly walking the streets. They crowded the brownstone stoops or the fire escapes in the evenings and hoped in vain for a cool breeze that would let them sleep at night.

Even with this pall upon it, New York was still a shock of noise and rushing movement, crowds of people and a babel of different languages. Immigrants were pouring into the city from Europe. Strange tongues, strange costumes, strange foods and habits put their stamp of cosmopolitan life upon this great seaport. The streets were thronged with vehicles of every kind—from the huge wooden brewery carts drawn by ponderous, massive horses, four teams linked together, to the dainty

broughams and carriages with their graceful, thorough-
bred horses, to the pushcarts pulled by human hands—
all clattering noisily over the rough cobblestones and all
raising clouds of dust for the eyes of the pedestrians.
Over the general hubbub of wheels and human voices
rang out the hawkers crying their wares: the vegetable
women, the applecarts, the milkmen who poured their
thick, cream-clotted liquid from huge vats directly into
the jugs of the housemaids, the vendors of shoelaces and
buttons, handkerchiefs and scarfs; the chimney sweeps
and the men who trundled cakes of ice in wheelbarrows,
chipping off bits of it for a penny; and lately—an innova-
tion by the publishers of the *World*—newsboys yelling on
the street corners.

The heat, the noise, the strangeness—none of these
daunted Nellie. She was young and she was strong. In
fact, the uproar of the great city stimulated and thrilled
her.

The great city, though, wanted nothing whatever to do
with her. No one would hire her. No one would even take
her seriously.

For weeks she had tramped the pavements and the
cobblestones of New York besieging the newspaper publishers. No editor in his right mind would give a woman
a job on his paper; this was the verdict she got and she
was made to feel it in every possible fashion—insultingly,
patronizingly, kindly, fatherly, curtly, with unnecessary
humiliation. The *Times*, the *Tribune*, the *Sun*, the *World*
—at the *World* she had not been allowed to speak to anyone but a copy boy, and the others had been almost as
bad.

She had even written to John Cockerill of the *World*,

offering as a stunt to go up in the balloon ascension sponsored by the paper in St. Louis. Cockerill had answered the letter, expressing his interest—but also his regret. And now she could not even get in to see him.

The stout courage, the high hopes, slowly ebbed away. She was reaching desperation when one day the final blow fell. She was robbed of her purse while she sat on a bench in Central Park. All of her money was gone. She was penniless, stranded, jobless.

That night she cried in great, shaking sobs of despair.

This was the end. She would have to give up, go home, beg Madden to give her her job back. But strangely, even as she was at last admitting her failure, something in her rebelled. She sat up on her hard, lumpy boardinghouse bed, pushing her hair back from her tear-soaked face. How could she go back? There must be a way for her to stay here. Had she really fought hard enough? Had it been too easy for her before, walking into Madden's office that first day and walking out with an assignment?

The next day she determined to make her last try. If it failed she would go home.

She got off the trolley at the corner of what was called "Park Row"—the row of newspapers and journals. She walked quickly past the *Day Book,* past the *Tribune* offices, past Baker and Godwin, Printers, past the Currier and Ives Building. She crossed the street to where the *Times* majestically occupied the whole triangle apex of two converging streets, but she gave it hardly a glance. She was on her way to the building with the gold dome.

Why a gold dome? The New York *World* had once belonged to Jay Gould who had treated it not only as a newspaper but as a means to further his own financial schemes. It was nothing, without reputation or sub-scribers, when Joseph Pulitzer bought it. In a few short years he had transformed it into one of the country's foremost newspapers and he had built a big gold dome over it that could be seen through most of the windows of New York—to flaunt his success in the eyes of the other Park Row publishers who had once laughed at him.

Nellie walked up the broad steps into the small dark lobby and up to the low gate and railing that separated this lobby from the busy offices beyond.

"I want to see Mr. Cockerill," she told the guard.

"I'm sorry, miss. No one can see him today. That's orders."

She rested her gloved hands on the top of the gate. To the dismayed eyes of the guard it was as if she had taken a grip that only force would break.

"I intend to see Mr. Cockerill. If I have to stay here all day and all night and all day tomorrow—I mean to see him. This is a matter of life and death for me."

"Oh, come, miss. It can't be that serious. Please—come back some other day. We're right on deadline getting out the Sunday paper and everybody is up to their necks in work."

She was wearing a thin summer dress of gray lawn trimmed in coral braid and a gray straw hat with a white veil. In spite of the heat and the pounding fear and anger inside her, she managed to look coolly poised. "I repeat. If you don't tell Mr. Cockerill I am here, I will wait right at this gate all day long."

"She'll soon get tired of that game," the usher con-fided to a reporter who was passing by. The reporter carelessly agreed, then looked at Nellie. He looked a second time and was not quite so sure. He had never seen such determination in a human face.

At any rate, this promised a little fun and variety to the day. He told a friend about it. The word spread like a chuckle through the main floor corridor, into offices and up the stairs. Reporters grinned at each other; a man from the circulation department popped his head out of his door to ask what the joke was all about; office boys who had been dodging work under the big back staircase suddenly found all kinds of errands that would bring them into the front lobby. They wanted to see the fun, too.

An hour went by. Two hours. The guard returned and he was angry this time.

"Miss, you will just have to leave. You're blocking passage for everybody coming in and going out, and I am not going to disturb Mr. Cockerill for you. The managing editor is a busy man. Now, do I have to make trouble for you?"

She was tired. Her legs were trembling with the strain of standing so long in one position; her back muscles ached with the effort to stand straight and tall. It was horrible to be threatened this way, worse even than being laughed at—and she was well aware of the laughter and the ridicule that was being directed her way—by the grinning faces, the open stares, the whispers and the jokes, by the way more and more of the copy boys found impudent excuses to come out front to get a look at her. Nellie was heartsick. She wanted to run away. If it were not for the desperation that gripped her, frantic and reckless, she would have done so. But she *would not go.*

"What am I going to do with her, sir?" the guard appealed to the advertising manager.

"Don't be a fool, Peters. Tell her to go. She's disrupting the whole place. All right! *I'll* get rid of her."

In three minutes he, too, was back, defeat and frustration written clearly on his face. Now the matter was getting serious. Should they call the police? He gathered up the head of the city desk, a circulation man, several reporters—the group growing and growing as he moved through the offices. They collected in the main corridor, arguing among themselves as to the best method of getting rid of this girl.

"Call the police—she's probably off her head, anyway. . . ."

"Let her stay there. She'll get tired. . . ."

"But why does she want to see Cockerill? He hates women—that kind of woman. . . ."

"She claims she was a reporter in Pittsburgh. . . ."

". . . call the police . . . no, don't, the other newspapers would use it against us. . . ." "Well, what else can we do?" "Maybe, if we talked to her again. . . ."

Someone laughed. It was Bill Nye, the paper's famous humor columnist and one of the great wits of his time. They all turned and looked at him. What was so funny?

"While you're standing there arguing, gentlemen, I think the matter has already been solved for you. Look" —he pointed past them down the hall toward the stairs leading to the next floor—"do you see what I see? The young lady seems to have taken the initiative out of your hands."

They looked and gasped. With their backs turned, while their attention was on their argument, Nellie had

[ 47 ]

quietly opened the gate and just as quietly walked down the corridor and past them—already going up the stairs.

"Here! You! You can't go up there!" The advertising manager moved to cut her off, but Bill Nye held him back.

"Oh, let her in. Anyone with that much determination deserves a break."

"But Cockerill—"

"Let Cockerill handle her. He'll send her packing. But if you want my opinion, I hope he doesn't. I admire that kind of courage."

The rest of them stared at him dumfounded. But in spite of themselves, one or two had been impressed the same way; they were reluctant to admit it but once Nye said it, they could, too.

"Sure—let her see him." "He'll eat her alive. . . ." "Let her have a chance. . . ."

The city editor cut it short. "So help me—all right! But when he comes roaring down here looking for somebody to put the blame on, just remember it wasn't me that wanted it. Nye, you'll have to be the goat. If I had my way it would be the police for her. Here, boy!" he signaled to an avidly interested, eavesdropping copy boy. "Run upstairs and find her. Show her the way to Cockerill's office. Don't try to explain to him. Just let her do her own talking!"

Nellie saw the boy coming, rushing up to her on the stairs. She wanted to cry and she was angry at the same time, angry at herself for her weakness of tears and angry at these stupid people who were going to stop her when she was this close to her goal. Well, she was past caring for her dignity. If they were going to stop her they would

[ 48 ]

have to send someone else besides a boy, because they were going to have to haul her off those steps physically!

The boy didn't touch her. He passed her. He turned, slightly. "This way, Miss. Follow me. I'll take you to Mr. Cockerill's office." The disdain and cheekiness in his voice failed to reach Nellie. She only heard the words: those unbelievable, undreamed-of words. She had made it! She had passed the barrier. The boy was her *escort*.

He led the way up the three flights to the big offices under the gold dome of the *World*. Nellie slowly followed. Now her knees were really shaking, both with the ordeal of her three hours of standing and with the reaction that set in now that she had won. She could hardly believe it.

In the torture of those three hours something had happened to her that was both good and bad. She had gained a strength she did not realize she possessed. In the core of her something had hardened and toughened, something that would stand her in good stead in the struggles she would face in the future. But she had lost, too—lost much of her youthful optimism, her buoyant expectancy, her trust in other people. A tiny seed was planted of self-will, of tough, egoistic self-preservation, and of suspicion that was always afterward to damage her relations with other people.

The top floor was quiet, its carpeted hall wide. The offices were big and few, and two of them bore the magical names in gold leaf: JOHN A. COCKERILL, MANAGING EDITOR, and the other adjoining it: JOSEPH PULITZER, PUBLISHER.

The boy knocked and opened the door—then fled.

A large desk occupied the center of the room. From

[ 49 ]

behind it the managing editor got to his feet. He was a big man, dignified and reserved. His mustache usually made him look stern and forbidding, but right now surprise and astonishment robbed him of his dignity. His mouth gaped.

"What is this? Young lady, what are you doing here? I gave instructions I wasn't to be disturbed!"

"I know. Don't blame the men downstairs. They did their best to keep me out. I'm Nellie Bly, Mr. Cockerill. I had to see you and I was determined to see you. It's too important to me to waste time being polite about it. I've stood down there and fought for three hours to get to see you and I wouldn't have done that if I hadn't thought it was just as important to you as it is to me!"

She moved to the desk and stood facing him. Even though her legs trembled, her voice rang with passionate sincerity because she was staking all on this: that she could convince him she was *necessary* to him, not that he was doing her a favor.

He pursed his lips. He was trying to remember the name. "Nellie Bly? Oh, yes, you sent me a letter. And then I had one from Madden in Pittsburgh. Good man, Madden. A good editor."

"Then you must respect his judgment. And *he* hired me—he didn't want me to leave *his* paper. I'm asking you for a job, Mr. Cockerill. I know"—raising a gloved hand to stop his protests—"you have all the good reporters you need, and if you did need more it wouldn't be a woman. To get this job I'd have to offer you something special, something different. Well, that's what I'm doing. I can give you stories that would be unusual, a kind you've never had in your paper before—no paper ever has!—for that matter. If Mr. Madden had faith in me to write what he called my sensational stories, can't you give me a chance? At least listen to me?"

"Sensational?" John Cockerill was cautious, but his alert newspaper sense came alive. He had been on the point of dismissing her, but the *World* was a booming, fast-growing newspaper coming up from nowhere to challenge the big, established press of the city, and to do so demanded new, fresh, out-of-the-ordinary approaches. "What do you mean by sensational?"

She had a small, thin book of clippings with her and she laid them on his desk. Then she sank into a chair. A horrible thing had happened. She found herself so weak she couldn't stand up, so wrought up her throat had choked to the point where she could hardly speak.

She tried to tell him of her work on the *Dispatch*, but it didn't sound capable; it sounded more like a child telling a grown man that she had behaved well in school that year. Cockerill put up a hand to stop her talking; he was completely absorbed in the clippings.

Slightly behind her, the connecting door between Cockerill's office and that of Pulitzer quietly opened. Nellie did not hear it. She wasn't aware that a tall, thin, powerfully built man with a large head had come noiselessly into the room. John Cockerill raised his head and saw, but the figure motioned him to silence.

Nellie swallowed. She began again to plead.

"That's the sort of thing I want to do here. I read every paper in New York every day. They all print the same things—yours is the only one that is different—but even you—it's still stories about Tammany Hall, stories about Mrs. Astor and Mr. Rockefeller, Jay Gould and

President Cleveland and finance and legislation. I want to write about the *other* New York. Since I've been here I've gone into every corner of the city—the wharfs, the Bowery, the tenements, the shops and factories—I've looked everywhere—and everywhere there are stories for you."

Cockerill studied her. He had lost his first anger at her bursting in on him; but even though he was beginning to listen seriously, he was still unwilling to accept what she said. "You're right about one thing. We do want those stories. But we make our own efforts to get them. The *World* has a reputation for being interested in the lives of the people of this city; in fact, we've been accused of bad journalism because we poke our noses in where they aren't wanted. What do you have to offer that is so different?"

She took a deep breath. This was the moment. If she could sell him now!— "I can give you *real* stories. From the inside. My idea is to actually work in the shops and then give you the story of what goes on inside them. I won't be just interviewing people; I'll share their experiences, put myself in their place. Think of the possibilities, Mr. Cockerill! Don't you want to know what a servant in a home really thinks, what the work is really like? You see people going into employment agencies— the *World* can have a reporter who actually goes in and applies for a job and finds out what it is like! Do you want to know what it is to be a sick person in a charity hospital, what kind of treatment he's getting? I'll *be* that sick person. Do you want an idea of what it feels like to be a prisoner in a jail or someone asking for relief from a social agency? You have good reporters. They give you their eyes and their ears to get the facts—but they can't get them all and they can't give you the emotion, the feeling, the distress and the suffering—because they don't live through it themselves. That's what I can give you. I'll go behind the scenes, and people will talk to me as they won't to an outsider. And my stories won't be just what someone else is willing to tell me; they will be *my own*, they will be about Nellie Bly working as a servant, or lying sick in a hospital or . . ."

"Turn around."

The deep voice, with its thick German gutturals, coming so unexpectedly behind her so startled Nellie that she flung herself around, out of her chair, her back to the desk.

The man who came slowly up to her and peered at her through unusually thick lenses with eyes that were almost blind was a stranger to her. Yet she knew him. His hand went out and touched her shoulder, and she knew that hand. Even in that slight impersonal touch she felt a nervous, potent strength that almost communicated words to her. A power emanated from him. A short, luxuriant Vandyke beard pointed up his thin, rough-carved face with haughtiness, impressiveness. Otherwise it was an ugly face.

She knew the face immediately. This was Joseph Pulitzer.

Not more than forty years old, he seemed an awesome sight to her eyes. This was the man who had emigrated to America a penniless youngster, an Austrian who spoke no English—yet this fabulous man now owned two of the countries largest newspapers, had been elected to the Missouri legislature, fought a duel, been responsible as no other man had for the fact that the Statue of Liberty stood in New York's harbor and had been credited with electing a president of the United States. To his admirers he was a genius; to his enemies, a devil they regarded with superstitious awe.

His hand dropped from her shoulder. Courteously he motioned her to a seat, then took one himself. One arm rested on the desk, the other on the arm of his chair while his long, tapering fingers caressed the blue-veined temple of his forehead.

"Talk some more, please. I was interested. *What* shop? *What* hospital do you plan to go into? How? Can you fool some doctor into thinking you are sick?"

The thick *d* and *t*, the strongly accented vowels, were the heritage of his European background.

"Yes, I can if I have to." She named hospitals, orphan asylums, factories that hired women. "I can put on a shabby dress and pretend that I need charity and spend the night at The Home For Needy Women—I caught a glimpse of it the other day and I think if I were down and out I'd rather sleep in the streets than go there. I know where women rent sewing machines and take them home to sew dresses or what they call 'piecework.' The men who give them the materials are called 'sweaters' because that's just what they do—sweat those poor women for a few pennies a day. Then I talked to a woman yesterday who had a sister taken away to Blackwell's Island for the Insane. She was crying. She had heard terrible stories about that island."

"*You* could get onto that island?"

"Yes." She said it without pause, although this had not occurred to her before.

[ 54 ]

"How? I suppose you think you could pretend to be insane?" Pulitzer's voice was insulting, heavy with scorn.

If she said she could do it and then she failed—but she *wouldn't* fail! "I will pretend to be insane. I will get on that island and no one will ever suspect that I am a reporter. Isn't that a challenge, Mr. Pulitzer? If I could do that. . . ."

"If you could—if rabbits could fly." Then suddenly his whole face seemed to change, to become very still. There was a long pause, and silence. Seconds passed. Both Nellie and Cockrill stared at the motionless figure of the great publisher, caught in a breathless kind of tenseness that seemed to emanate from him. He was unaware of them, rubbing the back of one hand with the other in an unconscious but troubled manner.

When he spoke again it was with such a harsh, impetuous manner that it startled both of them. "Yes! I think you could." he said. "I am just crazy enough to think you could." Behind his thick lenses his eyes glinted. He nodded his head rapidly. "I like you. You don't think anything is impossible. When I came first to this country, everyone told me *no*. No, you cannot do this. No, you cannot do that. But I did it. They laughed because I ran, ran, ran—all the time. But I got the story and the others did not. I did not think anything was impossible. You are like that. You are so young and so anxious and so sure, and that is a good thing for a reporter to be. But aren't you afraid? The police wouldn't like it if you tried to fool them. And aren't you afraid of being locked up with crazy people, shut up on the island with them?"

He had, purposely she knew, picked out the toughest job to test her on.

[ 55 ]

"I've never been afraid of anything," she declared stoutly. It was not true; she had been afraid downstairs and she had been afraid in this very room, only a few minutes ago. But it wouldn't do to tell them that.

Pulitzer suddenly winced. He put a hand in front of his eyes to shield them. "Pull the shades, will you please, John?" he asked Cockerill. The editor hastened to obey, feeling guilty that he had forgotten one of the basic rules of the office—there must never be a crack of sunlight in a room when the publisher was there. Light was excruciatingly painful to his eyes, just as noise was unbearable to his nerves.

"Please, try me out on that story—if that is the one you want," Nellie found herself almost whispering. "I'm so sure of myself I will gamble with you. If I can get onto Blackwell's Island and get a story for you on the treatment of the insane, get in there by pretending to be insane myself, will you give me a job—as a reporter on the *World?*"

"If you can do that . . ." he left it dangling there. He was very thoughtful. "But why do you want so much to do this? You want to go out and do crazy stunts because they are a thrill? *Nein,*" he said, answering his own question. "It's more than that, isn't it? You care about what happens to those people. I, too, care about them." To the other two in the room it was as if he had gone away from them in his thoughts and was brooding alone. "I believe in democracy." The way he said it, the word democracy was a precious thing. "When I bought this paper in '83, I ran the first issue on May 10th—and I put in it a statement. It said the *World* was a ' . . . journal dedicated to the cause of the people rather than that of the purse potentates . . . that will expose all fraud and sham, fight all public evils and abuses—that will serve and battle for the people with earnest simplicity.' That is what I said. We have done that, too, eh, John?"

Though he looked at Cockerill, Nellie knew he was talking to her. She caught her breath, in hope and in dread. What did he mean to do about her? Would he take her up on her gamble?

"From every bit of information we've been able to receive, Blackwell's is not a very nice place—not for a young lady," Cockerill said.

But Pulitzer shook his head. "We will gamble with her, John. I think she will come to no harm. But," he added, turning to her, "you must stay there at least a week. You must not tell anyone you are a newspaperwoman. And you must do this all alone. We will not help you, not with the doctors or the wardens or with anyone. If you get a good story, then you will have a job here. I promise it."

Nellie's excitement blazed out of her eyes. She tried to thank them both at the same time, but she was incoherent and could only stammer. Quick tears came into her eyes.

Cockerell ushered her to the door. "You go home now and wait, Miss Bly. You'll be sent word when to try this stunt of yours. I'll need time to clear space for the story and check with our legal department on the risks—it may be a week or more before you hear from us. Leave your address at the desk downstairs as you go out."

She turned to go. Again Joseph Pulitzer did an unprecedented thing. Something from his own terrible, poverty-stricken youth—the times when he lived on a bowl of soup as a whole day's meal—came to his mind.

[ 57 ]

"Have you any money? Can you wait those few days or perhaps a week?"

"Oh!" she gasped. "I forgot!" She told them the story of her lost purse. "I can't even pay my rent!"

Pulitzer fumbled in his pocket and drew out a shabby old cloth purse. He fumbled with the clasp, opened it, tried to see the coins inside. His half-blind eyes could not distinguish one from the other, however, and he gave up. "Give her a voucher, John. Give her twenty-five dollars." Then, to Nellie: "We will call you. This money, this is not a loan, it is an advance on your salary. I feel it, *surely*, that you are going to bring us a fine story. And then you will work for me."

She didn't walk downstairs, she floated.

If it was not to her credit that she enjoyed her revenge, at least it was very human. She walked up to the guard. "You are to write down my name and address for Mr. Cockerill, so that he can get in touch with me." The guard was not impressed. "And you will please direct me to the cashier's office. I want to get this voucher cashed. It is an advance on my salary."

The guard's face remained impassive, but at the sight of Pulitzer's signature on the voucher his eyes were like marbles.

"Yes, miss. Come *right* this way, miss."

# 4

It was late in September, a humid, overcast day, when a neatly dressed girl in a brown suit and hat, gray veiled, walked into the Temporary Home for Females. This was a lodginghouse partly subsidized by the city, since it was run to afford friendless and homeless women a place to stay for a few nights while they looked around for more permanent quarters.

It catered strictly to "deserving" working girls.

The woman in charge, a slovenly, grumpy, bored individual, looked the newcomer up and down, noting with an envious and suspicious eye that the brown suit was fairly expensive.

"Well? Whaddya want?"

"A place to stay, just for a few days, if you can accommodate me." The girl spoke with a strongly marked Spanish accent. She seemed unhappy, but that might have been only because the cold and unattractive looks of the Temporary Home did not appeal to her.

"Your name?"

"Nellie Brown."

"Where's your luggage? We have to be careful. If you don't pay up, we keep your luggage."

The girl smiled, exerting herself to please this belligerent landlady. "I have no luggage. I am waiting for my trunks to come, Señorita."

"Señorita? Where do you come from?"

"Cuba."

The woman was satisfied. So that was the reason for the strange accent! She could not know that Nellie was remembering the accents of Mexico. Her quick ear made her an excellent mimic, good enough at least to fool this landlady.

She was given a room to herself and when the dinner bell rang she joined the others in the large dining room, quietly slipping into the chair assigned to her, quietly eating the undercooked cabbage and the overcooked roast. Around her fourteen other women chattered and gossiped, but her silence went without comment since she was new.

Her neighbor at the table finally asked her name.

"Nellie Brown."

"But you say that so funny—are you a foreigner?"

"I am from Cuba." But the look Nellie gave the whole table made them think they had better stop questioning her. Since she seemed angry and resentful, they dropped her and forgot her.

The meal over, most of the women went, arm in arm, up the stairs to the sitting room, leaving the strange girl to finish drinking her tea. They had settled down to their evening pursuits—some sewing, some just talking, one or two of them reading—when the door of the sitting room banged open. There was a rush of skirts, a chair overturned, and the strange girl flung herself into a corner on the floor.

For a moment they were too startled to move. Then one of them made a motion to go to her.

"Stay away! Stay away!" the Cuban burst into frenzied, hysterical weeping. "Don't touch me—I'm afraid of you!"

That was the last word she said. For half an hour she sat and rocked, crying louder all the time. If they spoke to her she only stared blankly at them for a second, then burst into tears again.

The landlady was called. She tried to force Nellie Brown to get up off the floor. The strange girl whispered to her that she was afraid for her life; all the rest of the women there were crazy; they were going to hurt her; if she only had her trunks there she could get her pistol and protect herself. "I always carried one at home," she cried, in a crazy, hard-to-understand mixture of English and Spanish.

The landlady was scared. She wanted no trouble in her house and had visions of all the other women packing their bags and leaving—in fact, some of them threatened to do so immediately. Unless this Cuban was removed they would not stay! She was insane; there was no question of that. At first the landlady was reluctant to take any action. Perhaps the girl was just overtired, or perhaps the strange city and strange people had genuinely frightened her.

But after a while even the landlady was forced to realize that something had to be done. Nellie Brown would not get up off the floor. She could not stop crying. There was something almost inhuman about the way she would stare, unseeing, about her.

A policeman was summoned.

[ 61 ]

"Don't you worry," he soothed the frightened huddle of women in the hallway outside the door of the sitting room. "I've handled plenty like her. She's harmless. Now I want all of you to go to your rooms and lock yourselves in. I'll stay here outside the door and lock *her* in. Then in the morning I can take her before the judge and have her examined."

For a long tme the sobbing of the Cuban could be heard all over the upper floor of the house. Finally, when Nellie decided she had alarmed them sufficiently and convinced the policeman, she fixed herself a comfortable bed on the sofa and slept soundly for the rest of the night.

Judge Duff, who examined her the next day, did so in a hurried, unconcerned fashion. He heard what the policeman said, the testimony of the landlady, looked at 'Nellie Brown's' staring, blank eyes and then made up his mind. She was crazy, all right. But for form's sake she would have to go before a panel of experienced doctors.

This was what she had feared. This would be the test. Could she really fool medical men whose practice and experience would tell them the difference between sanity and insanity—and faked emotions?

She was brought in an ambulance to a hospital and into a clinic room where five doctors had hastily assembled. These were sober, dignified, highly respected members of their profession. One and all they fixed her with stern, suspicious eyes, talking about her as if she could not hear or understand them.

"No trembling . . . shows no fear . . . highly nervous . . . a normal woman would be frightened . . . Look at her eyes . . . distended . . . staring . . . rigid. . . . It's the usual thing . . . says the other women are crazy and is afraid of them . . . all insane people think others are insane. Uncontrollable fits of weeping, the policeman says. No question about it, extreme melancholia. . . ."

Only one doctor, a man by the name of Howard, was unconvinced. His examination was not as superficial as the others. By this time Nellie found it impossible to dredge up another tear, so she relied on keeping her eyes wide open, without blinking, staring over their heads as if she saw something there that they could not. She hoped to give the impression of having retreated into a world of her own. She was quiet and obedient, but when they spoke to her it was as if she didn't hear them—they had to push her to make her move or walk.

Dr. Howard was not sure. "It's her eyes. Every once in a while I seem to detect real intelligence in them."

"But Doctor!" another of his colleagues cried indignantly. "Look how fixed they are—and motionless. To get that wide stare so constant, she would have had to use belladonna in them. And I am sure she has used no drug. Besides, why should anyone of intelligence pretend to insanity?"

This was what she had counted on: that they would be fooled simply because they could not conceive of any woman's acting insane if she weren't! But Nellie almost gave the game away—for a second she was so indignant that anyone might have thought she had used a drug that she could not keep her eyes from flicking with outrage! Luckily, Dr. Howard was speaking to another doctor and his attention was diverted for the moment.

All five doctors certified her as mad. They signed the papers. She was committed to Blackwell's Island.

[ 63 ]

She was so elated over her victory that twice more she was close to discovery. In the ambulance going over the bridge to the island, Nellie was the only passenger besides the guard. She ignored him; her success so far had made her too confident. The guard, watching her, became uneasy—but for a reason Nellie could never have expected or anticipated, and certainly one that it would have been impossible for her to have done anything about, even if she had known!

In an interview weeks afterward, the honest guard stated what had been the basis for his doubts. "I began to think there was something wrong with that girl because she was the only crazy woman I ever conducted to the island who didn't try to jump on my lap and make love to me. They all do it—but not her. I wondered if I shouldn't say something, but I decided I'd only make a fool of myself."

The second hazard was Warden O'Rourke. Actually setting foot inside the asylum building, actually knowing that the papers had been signed and that she, Nellie Bly, was really launched into this strange adventure, made her reckless. Success went to her head. O'Rourke happened to look up at the moment he was signing her name and description into his official ledger, and he saw her stuff her handkerchief into her mouth. He could not know it was to keep herself from shouting out loud in her triumph, but he could not overlook that flash of high glee that crossed her face.

What was this?

He shut the ledger and crossed the long room to where she was standing. He bent down and looked closely into her face, her eyes. But he must have been mistaken: there was nothing there. Nellie Brown had no more intelligence in her face than had the rest of the inmates on the island. In fact, some of them, the borderline cases, had a great deal more.

Satisfied, he called the matron.

If Nellie had enjoyed herself up to this point, now came the rude awakening. To the matron she was just another one of these troublesome, hateful loonies who would learn to behave herself here or the matron would know why!

Nellie found herself being grabbed roughly by one arm, yanked out of the room and into the corridor. A long line of inmates passed her. Nellie stared at them, unbelieving. Could these be women?

Granted that they were not in their right minds, could that be the only reason for the misery on their faces—for the fearful way they avoided the matron and scuttled by her? Nellie's newspaper instincts came into quick life and she forgot the role she was playing. She became so interested in this, her first glimpse of the inmates, that she lagged behind the matron.

"Hurry up! Don't let her catch you!" came a soft whisper from that line of women.

Startled, Nellie looked up, saw the matron already disappearing through a door at the side and ran after her. All her fixed ideas were being turned upside down: she had imagined that she, being sane, would find herself with nothing in common with the others, that if she were to talk to anyone at all it would be to the personnel of the institution. But now it seemed that her first and only kind word had come from one of the inmates—and she was sure she and the matron were going to find themselves very quickly on opposite sides of a fence.

She was right. The big, bulky figure of the matron loomed over her. "When I tell you to follow me I want you to do it, do you hear! You'll learn to obey or I'll know the reason why." Nellie found herself shoved onto a hard bench in a reception room where some ten or more other women also waited.

A pretty woman sitting next to her leaned forward. "Who sent you here?"

"The doctors," Nellie answered.

"But why?"

"They say I am insane."

"Insane?" The woman shook her head. "It cannot be seen from your face."

Again Nellie was confused. This woman who talked so kindly and rationally—was she mad? Plainly dressed, she was quiet and ladylike. Obviously she was not completely mad because she had seen in Nellie the truth—the truth that had escaped doctors, judge and matron. Nellie knew nothing of modern psychology. Although superstition and ignorance about the question of mental illness were prevalent in that day, doctors were claiming to know how to cure. They were beginning to make strides toward scientific treatment; long medical papers were being published showing the different grades between the violently, incurable insane and those with only slight mental disturbances. No longer were the insane chained in dark, foul dungeons. There was supposed to be an attempt at healing.

She resolved to test it. She would no longer pretend to be insane. She would tell the truth and declare that she was absolutely normal, demand attention—and see what happened.

In the meantime, events were moving rapidly. When her turn came she was shown into a room, stripped roughly of her clothes and given an old patched and faded dress to wear which neither fitted her nor covered her properly. Her purse was taken away, even the hair-pins out of her hair, and she walked out of the reception room with nothing of her own identity remaining. Nellie Brown was no longer a person; she was just a name and a number. At least to the matron she had become one of the faceless, formless women like all the others.

A nurse herded all the newcomers, miserably dressed in their tattered garments, into an upstairs sitting room. Sitting room! It could hardly be less worthy of the name. Bare, cold and cheerless, it was, the gray walls discolored and stained and dirty, its chairs hard and uninviting—no books, no pictures, no curtains at the windows. The only redeeming feature was a big upright piano.

The asylum doctor was waiting there for them. He gave each a quick looking-over, seeming far more inter-ested in whether they were clean and free of lice than he was in their mental condition or their complaints. When it was her turn Nellie decided to put her decision to the test.

As quietly, as normally, as persuasively as she could, she told him: "Doctor, there has been a mistake. I have just come from Cuba and I was frightened and upset in a strange city. For a little while I became very disturbed. But I am as sane as you are. I am not sick and I do not want to stay here."

He paid absolutely no attention. He was not even interested.

One of the women had begun to cry. Several others, really mentally sick, were restless, muttering to themselves. The doctor turned to Nellie.

"You play the piano?"

When she said yes, he and a nurse led her over to the big walnut piano. They sat her down. She touched the keys. The piano was so badly out of tune that the sound made her shudder. When she remarked on this the nurse said, with real spite and venom: "That's a pity. We'll have to get one made to order for you."

Like both doctor and matron, the nurse, too, was an enemy. Reluctantly, this was what Nellie came to understand: that she had little to fear from the asylum inmates. Her only enemies were the asylum nurses, the guards and the matron who treated her and the rest with cruelty and violence.

That first evening she was made to stand in line in the freezing cold corridor while dinner was being prepared. The doors were flung open; they were ordered in, shoved in, pushed in. The smell of the food was sickening; the smells that came in waves from the dirty kitchen were even worse. They sat down on the hard benches and were given a slice of stale bread. In front of each place was a saucer of prunes and a bowl of tough, stringy meat with blobs of yellow fat on it—meat that only those with the strongest stomachs and the strongest teeth could eat. Nellie left hers, but it was immediately grabbed by a huge woman who had been in the place a long time and was used to the food. Nellie saw at a glance there was no use complaining either to the nurse or the cook about the

[ 68 ]

food. The nurse prowled up and down behind the backs of the women, yelling at those who didn't eat, yelling at others who ate too fast, slapping one inmate who spilled her bowl on the table.

Hungry, miserably conscious of the cold through her thin dress, her courage in coming here beginning to fade in the horrible reality of the place, Nellie went with the others back to the sitting room. Was this all that was provided for the whole day: this room, the quick trip to the dining room three times a day, then back to sit in idleness for the rest of the time? No, the nurse brought a needle and thread to one woman so that she might sew up a tear in her skirt. The others looked on with great interest; it was plain that many of them wanted desperately to have something to do and they envied this fortunate one—even though the nurse stood over her every second.

Again Nellie wandered to the piano. At least she might provide them with some diversion. She played a simple melody, a song that was gay and lively.

It was as if sunlight had poured into the room. Faces lit up. They crowded around the piano, begging her for more. The nurse looked on sourly, tempted to stop it but at the same time glad that it gave her a chance to slip away and eat her own good supper. (Nellie found out later that the asylum staff had special food and special service.)

For an hour she played, going from one request to another. In that hour even the most disturbed of the patients grew quiet and content.

The nurse returned.

"All right! Stop that, now. Bedtime."

A thin murmur of anguish swept through the older inmates, the ones who had been through this before. One of the new ones, a young girl, pressed close to Nellie. They were both suddenly fearful. The reaction of the others made them wonder, especially when they saw some of the bigger ones resist leaving the room by force. But the nurses were stronger and finally they were all shoved out.

When it was Nellie's turn, the other girl still clung to her. They went out together, hurried down the hall to the bathroom. Big tubs were anchored into the rough concrete floor; there was nothing else in the room except a pile of clothes in one corner. Three nurses stood like sentinels by the doorway.

One of them grabbed Nellie. Another one yanked her dress off over her head, stripped off her underclothing with swift, careless motions and pushed her toward the tub. "Get in there," she was ordered. Nellie put one foot in the tub, then jumped out, indignantly.

"It's ice cold! And this place is freezing—do you want me to catch pneumonia?"

"Get back in there and don't argue! Do you think we have time to go heating up water for your ladyship?" The two nurses could have made six of Nellie in size and weight, and they picked her up bodily and plunged her in. The shock made her gasp. The water was so cold it was almost unbearable, but she had no time to think of it.

Almost before she was in, another inmate was handed soap and a brush and told to begin scrubbing. Nellie protested she could do it herself, but her protests went unheard. The other inmate blindly and fearfully went about her task, almost taking the skin off Nellie's face and back

[ 70 ]

and scalp in her anxiety to do a good job and not be scolded by the nurses. In the other tubs the other new patients were getting the same treatment; the young girl, fragile and thin and really sick, was sobbing with pain inflicted by the brutal scrubbing. Even their hair was washed—and left to dry of itself in the cold air.

The scrubbing had at least warmed Nellie a little. When it was over she rinsed herself off and prepared to climb out. Suddenly, totally unprepared, she was caught right in the face with a violent splash of ice-cold water. Three bucketfuls were poured over her head!

"Stop that! Haven't you any feeling for—"

Another bucketful, reserved by the nurses for just such unruly patients, was emptied over her, effectively stopping her mouth and her protests. Shivering, she climbed out and was handed a rough towel with which to dry herself; and then a thin flannel slip with the label stenciled in back: Lunatic Asylum, BIH 6.

The girl in the other tub was in very bad shape. Physically unwell before she was admitted, she was now in real agony. She could not stop crying; her face was white; the thin bones of her shoulder blades seemed sharp enough to pierce her skin as she huddled, protesting, pleading, trying to escape the ice-cold drenching. But it did no good. Even when the nurses saw that she was too cold and feeble now even to dry herself, they were only the rougher and more exasperated as they had to do the toweling for her.

She, too, was handed a flannel slip.

This was more than Nellie could stand.

"Can't you see she is ill? She'll die of the cold with

[ 71 ]

only that thin slip! Can't you at least give her a warm nightgown?"

"We don't have nightgowns here. This is charity."

"But the city pays to keep up these places and pays people like you to be kind to the unfortunates brought here."

This kind of talk—this independence, this calling them to account—was so unprecedented that all the nurses stopped their work to stare at her. One of them, the biggest, folded her arms and advanced threateningly on Nellie. "You'd better understand something—you don't need to expect kindness here, for you won't get it. Understand?"

Their words angered her more than the treatment had. They were not unconsciously unkind, then. They were deliberately so, and knew exactly what they were doing. She thought to herself that probably they even enjoyed it!

The treatment was too much for the sick, fragile girl. In the sitting room she had sat on the bench near Nellie while the piano playing had been going on. Nellie had been impressed by the struggle she made to keep her mind balanced and clear; the efforts to speak clearly and sanely; the way in which the girl realized where she was and why—and her determination not to go completely under. But the ice-cold bath snapped her slender thread with reality. For a little while, even after that, while the two of them huddled in their freezing beds the girl tried to snatch back her sanity; she sang to herself, brokenly, some of the music Nellie had played; she talked to herself, reassuring herself.

"Shut up!" yelled one of the nurses, clumping down

the big dormitory in her hard leather boots. "Stop that singing! If you don't stop I'll make you."

It was too much. The girl went into sudden spasms and convulsions, shaking the bed in her agony. The flickering light of sanity went completely out of her mind, her face, her voice. She was hustled out of the room and put into a barred cell where her ravings would not disturb the others.

In the story Nellie was to write to the *World*, her flaming, passionate hatred at this treatment blazed forth:

Insane? Yes, insane. And as I watched insanity creep over a mind that had appeared to be almost all right, I cursed the doctors, nurses and all public institutions for their stupidity. I resolved I would by every means make my mission of benefit to my suffering sisters. Criminals are given every chance to prove their innocence. These poor, overworked girls are convicted after a few trifling questions.

But long before she was to get out of this place and write such lines, there was more to come.

The next day she asked to be allowed to go to the bathroom. She was told it was locked for the day. Only her vehement protests unlocked it for her and a couple of the other women. But there she saw some other newcomers, who were undergoing the same bath treatment— and she realized they were using the same towels she had had the night before. And when they were finished with them, they were again handed to Nellie. She refused; she would dry her hands on her gown. One of the new arrivals had been covered from head to foot with open, erupting sores!

She saw elderly women dragged by the hair and shoved into closets, in order to keep them quiet. She saw girls slapped in the face when they spoke above a whisper. The food was so uniformly bad that most of the inmates were always hungry. Certainly they were always cold!

Beforehand, in Cockerill's office and while she had made preparations to get herself committed, Nellie's overriding fear had been of the "crazy" people themselves. She had had morbid fancies of weird things going on, even of physical danger from them. And it was true that there were times when her healthy mind recoiled from the manifestations of mental ill-health around her: the sudden, unexplained changes from good temper to bad; the outbursts of tears; the deathlike appearance of one woman who sat absolutely rigid and unmoving for hours at a time; the drooling mouths and shaking limbs.

As far as she could determine, the women's part of the institution was divided into a ward for violent cases, a "Lodge" where disobedient or unmanageable cases were thrown temporarily for safekeeping, and then the ward that she was in. It was not enough; there should have been more separation. The mildly disturbed cases should be by themselves so that they might have a chance to improve. If even she, healthy as she was, was affected by the unattractive symptoms of the more serious cases, think what effect it was having on those borderline cases who were making their brave, lonely fight to return to sanity!

The shocking part was that it was the nurses, not the inmates, who ill-treated her. Nellie soon saw that even those among them who were not deliberately cruel were at best thoughtless. They paid no attention to her pleas for warmer bedclothes. Night after night she huddled, freezing, sleepless except for broken snatches toward morning. And if she did manage to doze off, she would be awakened by the heavy clump of the nurse's boots striding up and down between the beds, flashing lantern lights into the patients faces to be sure they were quiet.

For the most part, the days were rainy. There was nothing to do, nowhere to go. They were not allowed to wander around. They could listen to Nellie's piano for only brief periods of time. *They could not even talk; they could only whisper to each other.* Yet Nellie made friends. Incredible as it seemed to her, she found herself making friends with some of the less disturbed women. One, in particular, found the means of telling Nellie that she knew she was cured. She was a married woman, and now she had come back to her right mind, she desperately wanted to go back to her husband and family. At first Nellie was cautious, but the more she talked to the woman, the more she was convinced that it was true.

The next visit of the doctor found Nellie determined. She argued with him, not only for herself but for the other. "Examine her. Examine me. You'll find we don't belong here. The least you can do is test us."

He patted her on the shoulder. "That is all right. You just be quiet. You'll be examined after a while. We have a time and place for that—all in good order."

There was nothing else she could do. She turned away and walked to the window. She could not stand the heartbreak on the other woman's face.

Once the sun came out and the inmates were let out into the yard. Nellie had looked forward to this because the confinement itself was hurting even her sound, healthy body. But what she saw there in the yard made her glad to escape back into the four walls. The nurses were too busy—or too lazy—to take inmates from different sections out at different times. They let everyone out at once. And Nellie's group, the mildly ill ones, were treated to the horrifying gruesome spectacle of seeing the violently insane from the other wards in the same yard with themselves.

True, the violent ones could do them no harm. They were *chained!*—all manacled to one long, thick iron cable.

But they were a terrible sight. And the sound of their screaming—their ravings, their tortured, obscene gibbering, their pitiful wails—haunted Nellie so that she could hardly sleep for many, many nights afterward.

"And think what a sight like that does to these other women! It's enough to drive them mad, even if they weren't mentally sick already," Nellie protested to a nurse.

"You watch your saucy ways or we'll send you to the Lodge," the nurse threatened.

Nellie kept quiet after that. She would do a lot to get her story, but being thrown into the Lodge, the ward where they kept the dangerously insane, was not part of her story. The *World* wanted the story, but they also wanted her alive and well enough to tell it.

On the tenth day came deliverance. She had not been sure of the arrangements that Cockerill would make for her delivery; she had even begun to fear it might mean a real battle to get her out. But it all happened very quietly and uneventfully. She was called out of the bedroom dormitory, and a worried and very subdued nurse ushered her politely into Warden O'Rourke's office, where she found a lawyer from the *World*.

"Thank God!" Nellie breathed.

Her clothes were handed to her, a carriage was waiting and almost in a dream Nellie found herself walking out of Blackwell's Island, the doors closing behind her softly. Had it really happened? Or was it still happening and was this just another of her own wishful dreams at night, back there in her cold, freezing bed in the dormitory? But it was true. She was free.

She went home to her boardinghouse and took a long, hot bath. Her body cried out for sleep, but her mind, tortured by the impressions of the last ten days, would not let her rest. Now—while the feeling and memory were so strong—*now* she must write it. Nellie sat down at her table and wrote for hours and hours, stopping only to eat a mouthful of food now and then. And under her pen not only the facts came alive, but her own fury and anger and disgust, her own passionate cry for justice for the poor, sick, helpless creatures caught up in the inhuman institution of Blackwell's Island—all this came alive in flaming words.

It would have to run as a series.

The first installment, "Behind Asylum Bars," was printed by the *World* almost as an entire page with hardly anything else on it to detract from its importance. John Cockerill read only a few lines of her copy when he recognized its tremendous importance. It was a "first" in journalism—the first of its kind, the first time anyone had actually penetrated into an insane asylum, actually lived through the experience. Although he had expected something unusual, he had not been prepared for the vivid style of writing that took the reader right with Nellie into Blackwell's Island.

Publication of "Behind Asylum Bars" was a bombshell.

It rocked the whole city. Before nightfall there was hardly a person in New York who had not read the story, or heard about it from someone else. The *World* could not keep up with the demand for copies; they printed more and more. And the paper printed its own editorial on her story, calling it, in truth, "the talk of the town and the nation."

Day after day the series ran. Interest grew, rather than lessened; mail addressed to Nellie Bly poured into the offices of the *World*.

A member of the Board of Charities came to Cockerill.

"We need your help. I don't know if this is a trumped-up story or not, but I hope not. Because if there is a Nellie Bly, we need her. For years we've been begging for more money, more appropriations so that a place like Blackwell's Island could have competent doctors, good nurses and scientific research. We were never able to get it. Nobody cared what happened to the insane as long as they were out of sight. Now everybody is complaining to us. But we don't care—not as long as this kind of publicity may force city officials to spend a little more money. But we need your Nellie Bly to help us. If she really is—I mean, if there is a girl named that and she did what she claims, then we want her to go back there with a delegation of us—point out the things that we have never seen ourselves."

Cockerill led him downstairs. Halfway through the

writing of her series, the managing editor had called Nellie in from her boardinghouse.

"You work *for* the *World*," he had said, simply. "And, like all the others, it is right that you work *at* the *World*." He had shown her her desk, right in the city room with the others.

She was glad to go with the delegation. And even though the asylum, convinced there would be such an investigation, had cleaned up the building, improved the food, supplied warm clothing and books for the inmates, it was obvious that all this was so new it could only have happened in the past few days.

On October 28th, the *World* was proud to run this story:

## THE WORLD THEIR SAVIOR

### How Nellie Bly's Work Will Help the City Insane

"Dr. MacDonald and President Simmons of the Board of Charities asked for an increased appropriation for their work. The city gave it immediately. The appropriation for Blackwell's Island has now been raised to $160,000. An additional $201,387 has been granted for other city asylums for the insane. Better food, salt and meat and better-cooked food have been ordered.

Much of the new appropriation will be allocated to more doctors, at least one to every ten patients. The pay for doctors has been raised, so that a higher type of physicians may be secured. . . .

This announcement was a proud moment for both Pulitzer and Cockerill. Even though papers all over the country had picked up Nellie's story, some rival publications of the city had labelled it sheer sensationalism and criticized them for allowing a young girl to take such chances. This was their vindication. The story had led to really sound, decent changes for the betterment of the unfortunate mental patients.

Nellie was proud, too. But because she was—and always would be—a newspaperwoman first and a crusader second, she was prouder by far of something else. That "something else" was her desk in the city room—tangible proof that a turning point had been reached in her life.

It meant her undisputed right to call herself a reporter for the *World*.

# 5

The echoes of the Blackwell's Island story were a long time dying. Families who had relatives committed to insane asylums wrote to Nellie Bly, worriedly, asking if she would investigate this place or that one, find out if their Uncle James or their Aunt Emma were being well taken care of or being brutalized. Letters came from cranks, from people with medicines or pills that would cure insanity if only they—or Nellie—could get the money to manufacture them. But there were also solid, thoughtful letters from civic leaders who had long felt the need for reform in public institutions like Blackwell's; they hailed her work as a ground-breaking sort of thing that would make their efforts that much easier.

On the *World* staff reactions were as varied as the individual nature of the men themselves. On the staff were many of the ablest reporters, shrewdest news analysts and best feature writers of that day. Pulitzer had determined on a breezy, readable, wide-open paper that would break with all stuffy traditions, and the men he hired reflected that policy.

Regarding their attitude toward Nellie, some were admiring, some patronizing, some jealous, but all were curious about this strange little female. In Pittsburgh, Nellie had written her stories at home. At the *World*, however, she was given a desk in the big city room.

One and all they looked to Bill Nye for a lead as to how they should behave toward her. The famous wit and columnist stopped by her desk one day and perched himself on a corner of it.

"Miss Bly, meet Bill Nye. And if that sounds like a vaudeville routine, I can't help it. One of us has to change his—her—name. I think I've had mine longer than you have and I came by mine legitimately. You stole yours from Stephen Foster. I think you should give it back. Otherwise we're going to get mixed up in each other's mail."

"It isn't where I stole it from," she replied pertly, "it's what I do with it that counts. Maybe someday people will say 'wasn't there a song named after that newspaperwoman Nellie Bly?'" What started out as a small smile broadened to a genuine grin as she looked up at him, towering over her desk.

"Well, you really can smile! I bet Jim Cole that I would make you laugh. My reputation as a humorist was at stake because not one of us has seen you without that grim, determined look on your face—and we were thoroughly frightened of you, ma'am."

"I do not look grim!" Her twenty-year-old vanity was outraged.

"I never said that, either." The blond Jim Cole, assistant at the foreign news desk, edged up to them. "I said 'intense.'"

"That's better." To her own surprise she found herself enjoying this, at ease, entirely forgetful of the mail at her desk or her story of the mill girls on strike at the Clark Thread House. Some other reporters edged over, so that her desk was finally in the center of a circle.

"I must say, Miss Bly, you're a good sport. We were pretty worried when we heard you were going to be in here because we thought we'd have to be so careful of our language"—a young, pink-cheeked cub reporter blushed until his cheeks were even pinker—"but you don't seem to notice or anything."

She laughed. She sat sideways in her chair, her long, cinnamon-colored skirt brushing the unpainted wooden floor, a white starched frill under her chin the only relief from an otherwise severe costume. Ladies were not supposed to cross their legs, but in her new sense of freedom she did it without thinking. One small foot tapped the wastepaper basket as she talked. "You see, I *really* don't hear you. Shall I show you my secret?" She reached into a desk drawer and brought out something clenched in both hands. She held them up.

"Well, I'll be—!" Jim Cole was stunned. "Cotton! You put that in your ears, Miss Bly? And here we thought—we wondered . . ." they all exploded in laughter.

Inevitably it came—the same old question.

"How come you want to work on a newspaper, Miss Bly?"

"Well, I always wanted to write. And it's exciting—and fun." Remembering the nurses on the island, she shuddered. "Sometimes."

"Sometimes is right. But right now I've got a deadline to meet and not a thought in my head." Nye groaned.

"Yeah, and sometimes it's just plain awful," another man joined in. He sat on the other corner of Nellie's desk. "A friend of mine, reporter from Chicago, he was telling me he had to cover the trial of those anarchists, the Haymarket ones. Trouble was—this fellow said he sympathized with them all the time. Never did think there was any evidence they threw any bomb. He wrote it that way and his editor gave him a dressing-down and changed his story."

An argument raged around her. Should a newspaperman allow his personal feelings to enter into a story? Should he just report the facts? Was a man to stop thinking and feeling just because he was a reporter? What about his loyalty to the policies of the paper? Yeah, but what about his loyalties to his own ideals?

Nellie listened and loved it. This was real newspapermen's talk.

She was leaving for her boardinghouse at five o'clock that day when Jim Cole stopped her just outside the front doors. "I'd be honored, Miss Bly, if you would join me—and a friend of mine—at the Albion." Next door to the World Building were the offices of the *Army and Navy Journal*. The downstairs front rooms had been rented out as a public dining room called the Albion. "Some tea or coffee might make you feel not so tired."

"Why—thank you. Thank you very much, but I—yes, I will. I should like to go." She was remembering that they had called her "grim." "My mother always had tea about this time and I find I have missed it since I have been in New York."

Someone should have warned her that Cole had a reputation for playing pranks.

They walked inside the big dim, dark-paneled room. They made their way slowly through the crowd three

[ 84 ]

deep around the stone fireplace, dodged elbows and knees of people—it was too dark in there at first for her to see to whom the knees and elbows belonged—who were sprawled on the long oak trestle benches. They reached their table at the back and sat down.

This was the first moment she had had to really see the room. And then she knew. Cole had deliberately brought her into a place that was sacred to men only, frequented only by men. She was the only woman present. The faces turned toward her reflected astonishment and dismay, but one and all they were hostile. Written large all over them was the unanimous opinion that they resented her being there.

She was furious. Should she just get up and walk out?

Before she could act, Cole introduced his friend James Metcalf of the magazine *Life*. But Metcalf wasn't having any of this embarrassing situation. He muttered an acknowledgment of the introduction and rudely took off into a corner.

Cole also rose to go. The joke had gone on long enough.

But by now Nellie was too angry to give in. She signaled the waiter. "Tea, please. With cream."

"By George! This is going too far!" A near-by white-haired, white-bearded man clapped his hat on his head motioned imperiously to the same waiter. "When it comes to this—soon there won't be a single place in the whole town where a man can escape from these hussies!"

John Cockerill came in with Bill Nye. They took in the situation at a glance, the attention focused on that one table where Cole sat in agonized embarrassment, the girl stiff as a poker and the waiter hovering over her, undecided as to whether or not to fill her order.

The managing editor gave a swift glance around the room. He saw *World* reporters and he looked at each, his eyes giving a silent command. Then he moved to Nellie's table. And as he did so, other men came to join in his train, following him and Bill Nye. They were staff from the *World*—Anders of the city desk, Jerrold of shipping news, Bernstein who covered the police beat. Others drifted with them until eleven men converged on the big, lonely table.

It was the *World* against the Albion.

The waiter asked their order. With his puckish humor, Bill Nye spoke for all. "Tea, please. With cream." Somebody snorted. Nye was a great beer drinker.

Under cover of the general talk, Cockerill asked Nellie, "How did this happen? You surely weren't looking for a story in here, were you?"

She had been furious, but suddenly she wanted to laugh. Nellie Bly Investigates the Albion. Or How Men Act When They Think No Woman Is Watching—she could just see the headlines. She wanted to laugh, too, and maybe cry a little, because something very wonderful had happened to her. She had seen herself defended as the *World* would defend only one of its own. She belonged.

"Oh, it was kind of a dare, Mr. Cockerill. Silly of me, I guess."

Afterward Cole thanked her. "You really are a good sport, Nellie. It would have meant my job if Cockerill knew I had tricked you into going there. I'm glad you have such a good sense of humor," he added.

Going home that night she thought about it. Were they right? Was she too grim? Too serious about herself? She couldn't remember the last time she had played or had fun. Even laughing had become a rare thing. When she had been young the house had always been a bright, cheerful one, with charades and parlor games for the evenings and picnics—when was the last time she had been on a picnic? She was startled, realizing how rigid her life had become.

For that reason, Nellie was willing to listen when Cockerill proposed a change of story for her. They would do her ideas later, but right now he wanted something lighter.

So on Sunday, December 18th, the *World* ran a three-column story of Nellie's experiences in trying to learn ballet. Cockerill had been short of space; many more important events were crowding the paper; but her story was too good, too sprightly, too amusing—and his sound newspaper sense told him the readers would like their Nellie in this role.

The column began:

> I have been learning to be a ballet dancer. I have always had an almost manlike love for the ballet, and when I go to spectacular plays and to the opera I try to get close to the bald-headed row. Breathless with admiration I have watched the ballet twirl on its toes and spring into the air. . . .

But Nellie found there was a lot more to learning ballet than just the love for it, or a desire to make graceful poses and springs. She had to work and work hard. Muscles aching, her feet clumsy, her body a stolid little earth-bound thing unable to follow the quick and graceful ballet master, she wrote with a delightful and saucy sense of humor that poked fun at herself. Her pride had taken a thumping fall and she let the whole of New York in on her crestfallen state.

Probably what her readers loved most about her tale of woe was her acute embarrassment at being, for the first time in her life, in front of strangers clad only in a tunic, with her legs bare and unhidden by long skirts. She tells how she "clutches her tunic skirt" in front of her as she sidled into the room, not quite believing that she wouldn't be hauled into a police court for being so brazen. How cold and bare she felt—how shockingly nude!

Cockerill was right. The *World* readers were charmed with the story.

Several weeks after that, two young men walked rapidly up Sixth Avenue. A light snow had fallen on the city. The sun was out, but while it made the snow sparkle radiantly, it gave little heat. The two shivered in their overcoats, watching their breath come out in short puffs of steam as they talked.

The stout one caught the tall, thin one by the sleeve.

"Jim, do you see that woman over there? What do you suppose she's up to? Looks like she's following that old man. She's acting very suspiciously."

"Very odd," James Metcalf agreed.

The woman they had noticed, walking some thirty paces in front of them, did indeed deserve attention. She would walk slowly a step or two, stop, pretend to be looking at a store display, slide along the building, then take a few quick steps, bumping into people who got in her way. She was doing all this, it seemed, so that she could keep her eye on a ragged old man without his noticing her.

That was Metcalf's opinion. "He doesn't seem to know she's watching him. Look!—now he's turned. He's coming back our way. Let's see if she follows him. Maybe she's his wife. No, she's dressed peculiarly but she's well dressed."

The old man wandered up to them, aimlessly. Just in front of them he suddenly stopped, reached down to pick up something that was lying on the snow. It was a crust of bread.

"Poor old fellow," muttered the stout man. Both he and Metcalf reached into their pockets. What were a few pennies to them—when this old man was starving and cold? He hadn't asked them for anything, seeming happy with the crust he had found, but they pressed their coins on him and were overwhelmed by his pathetic gratitude.

He went his way. Turning, they found themselves face to face with Nellie Bly.

"You fell for it!" she said indignantly. "You are the first man he has tried that trick on. Mostly it has been women. He's a fraud. I've been watching him. He carries that crust of bread up his sleeve and drops it just in front of his victims. You can't catch him at it because he is clever; he's quick—and you are so upset because he—"

"Well, I'll be—"

"Oh, it's Mr. Metcalf!"

The other man had started off in hot pursuit of the beggar.

"Yes. I didn't recognize you at first, although I saw

[ 89 ]

you playing detective. I'm sorry we kept you from catching him."

Nellie shook her head. The cold had brightened her cheeks to a glowing pink. Her eyes were sparkling. "I wasn't trying to catch him. He probably *is* very poor. I just wanted a story out of it."

Metcalf's stout friend came up, panting and disappointed.

"He got away. Tell me what you saw, miss," he said, whipping out pencil and paper. "I'm a reporter for the *Tribune* and—"

"Hold it, Nels. Miss Bly is a reporter, too, and this is her story."

"Oh! Nellie Bly! From the *World.* All right, tell you what—since I ran my legs off trying to catch your swindler, you do your piece and call it 'Nellie Bly Sees Beggar Fraud at Work." Then I'll do a piece for my paper and call it 'I Saw Nellie Bly See a Beggar Fraud at Work.' Then Jim, here, can do one of his famous satirical stories on how *he* saw a veteran *Tribune* reporter outsmarted by a lady *World* reporter. What do you think of that?"

They all laughed. Then Metcalf said, "I'll do it if only to make up to Miss Bly for my rudeness one day at the Albion. But I have an even better idea. It's too nice a day to write anything. I have a friend who has a sleigh and a team of horses. Why don't the three of us go for a ride in the country?"

"Make it four." Agreed Nellie, with a promptness that surprised her. "I borrowed this coat from a friend. You see, I have a confession to make. That beggar took me in first. Then, when I caught on to him, I was afraid he'd recognize me so I traded coat and hat with a friend of mine, in front of Wallach's. Poor Agnes—she's probably freezing in my coat that's too small for her—and I can hardly walk, her's is so big for me."

That was the beginning.

The next few months were ones of completely new experiences for Nellie. For the first time since her father's death she learned again how to play. She learned to laugh and relax and have fun. Among the newspapermen of the city there was a camaraderie that now reached out to include her. Evenings were spent in the homes of several married couples, playing wild card games of lotto, dressing up for charades, putting on amateur plays written by the more talented among them. There were visits to plays and musical comedies. There were sleigh rides and skating in Central Park.

Nellie's escorts were usually Jim Cole, Anders or Metcalf. But neither she nor they thought of themselves as beaux. What they did, they did as a group.

During this time she worked hard, but the stories were the lighter kind that required little effort on her part, and were somehow all mixed up with the glorious, exuberant novelty of playing, so that work itself was as much laughter as it was seriousness.

At least half the working reporters in town had front-row seats at the Academy of Music the night Nellie made her debut there as a chorus girl. The ballet school story had been such a success she had decided to follow it up with one on how she tried to go on stage.

The result was riotous. The story of the show was a crazy mixture of Greeks and gladiators and Amazons. The chorus came on stage, thirty girls all dressed in silver tights, helmets on their heads and carrying spears and shields. They kicked and danced in perfect rhythm to the music, making a flashing display of feminine beauty and dancing ability across the footlights—all in step, all in perfect time.

Except for one girl.

This one girl seemed to know nothing of what she was supposed to do. When the line went one way she went the other. When they kicked she was twirling around. When they twirled she kicked. Her helmet slipped down, her wig went awry—and the newspapermen in the first five rows exploded into bowls of laughter. It was Nellie!

The audience, at first bewildered and not at all pleased, soon caught on to the joke. The whole house rocked with laughter. Even the hero, singing a love song as the chorus line cavorted around him, was having trouble keeping his own face straight. There was a quick glimpse of a furiously angry stage manager who so forgot himself for a second that he stepped from the wings into plain sight and shook an impotent fist at this dancer who was so disrupting the performance.

What made it even more funny was that Nellie was not deliberately making mistakes; she was honestly trying to keep in step. The climax came when the chorus line divided, half the girls going to one side of the stage, another to the opposite side. Nellie apparently had not heard of this plan and went on kicking wildly in front of the hero. She and he were alone until suddenly she saw her predicament and ran a few steps this way, reversed herself, ran the other way, tried to find her place in line and succeeded only in throwing all thirty girls completely into choas.

The audience went wild. Men stood up and pounded each other on the backs, tears running down their cheeks in helpless laughter. Finally the curtain came down.

Nellie's story the next day was headed "Nellie Bly On The Stage." It began:

> I made my debut as a chorus girl or stage Amazon last week.
>
> It was my first appearance on any stage and came about through reading among the *World* advertisements one that called for . . . girls for a spectacular appearance. So I found myself one afternoon. . . .

And it went on to tell how she was hired, given no training but told just to follow the girl in front of her. It was a masterpiece of good-natured poking fun at herself, going into details of how *she* felt facing that audience, and how the audience must have felt watching her.

In a subsequent story she took up fencing. Then there was a slightly more serious one in which she exposed a mesmerist, but even here her high spirits came through. It had little of the indignation of her earlier stories. Nellie was too happy, too gay, too full of the joy of living to be touched deeply.

She discovered the innocent vanity of pretty clothes. Amazed at herself, the hours when she was not working were crammed with the selection of clothes, fittings and the delight of wearing them for the compliments they brought her. She reveled in fur muffs and handsome little velvet bonnets edged with soft white fur to frame her glowing face; a new skating costume of bottle-green trimmed with the sauciest of peach and ivory-colored ribbons, the full skirt daringly raised to above her shoetops. And what a dress it was!—for the frosty, starlit nights of skating on the pond with a crowd of ten adventurous souls, the laughter and the jokes and the girls pretending to be frightened at going so fast, and the lovely feeling of the skimming motion that was like wine rising to her head, making her want to sing and laugh and cry all at the same time, feeling the strong, intimate pressure of the man's hands that gripped hers—and then the bonfire at the edge of the ice with its warm blaze the only thing besides themselves that was alive and awake at that hour of the night! Then there were party dresses and the heavy silk cloaks to go with them—no protection against the cold of the night, but who cared about that? They were so pretty and so much admired!

They were all young, and being young they were reckless with time. Getting married, getting settled down with families and houses and property—that still for the future; not now, not for them. This was the time for just sheer fun.

Nellie threw herself into it as wholeheartedly as she did everything else. It was as if some premonition told her that this mood, this time, could only be a temporary one for her and she must enjoy it to the hilt. The climax and her triumph came with the annual Press Club Ball. For the first time she wore a ballgown. It was made of white satin and trimmed with red rosebuds, cut low over her shoulders, figure-tight in front and with an enormous, stylish bustle in the back. If ever in her life she was pretty, she was that night—as much by the radiance of her big gray eyes as by the art of the dressmaker.

Bill Nye bent low over her hand. "Did we ever say you were grim, Nellie? Did anyone ever doubt that you were a woman? On behalf of all doubting Thomases I hereby tender our apologies."

But as abruptly and suddenly as it had started, all this came to an end. Playtime was over.

Cockerill summoned her to his office.

"Nellie, what do you know of a man called Edward R. Phelps? The one they call the 'king'—king of the lobby-ists—the Fox?" he asked.

6

The whole state structure of New York was rotten, through and through, with corruption, graft, bribery, outright stealing of public funds from the state treasury, rake-offs on state-appointed jobs, even the buying of votes of state senators. And throughout the state there was a network of rottenness which centered in the state capitol at Albany, and owed its system and organization to one man—the big boss lobbyist Edward R. Phelps.

He was called the "king" and known to have a finger in nearly every pie where a dishonest penny was to be found. He was ruthless, unscrupulous and connected with the underworld of criminals. Nevertheless, he oper-ated so openly, so brazenly, that Nellie had no trouble at all in finding him.

It was three days after her talk with Cockerill.

Phelps was staying at the Kenmore Hotel in Albany. Nellie went from the railroad station first to Stanwix Hall, a discreet residential hotel, to freshen up after her trip from New York. It was important that she look just right for the part she was to play.

She surveyed herself in the long pier mirror. She must

look matronly, well-to-do, a respectable married woman. The conservatively cut black bombazine dress was a fine twilled fabric with a silk sheen to it. Nellie had generously padded her hips, but to keep from looking too mature she wore a hat, an expensive one, smartly decked out with red and green ribbons. She pinned an expensive brooch to the neck of her dress, which added just the right touch, and now she was satisfied. Phelps would notice it and think her just a little bit vain, greedy for money, more interested in the material luxuries than in any such silly things as honesty and integrity.

She walked to the Kenmore.

There was a lonely, scared feeling in the pit of her stomach. In asking her to do this job, to try to trap this wiliest of foxes, Cockerill had not spared her his own worries about it. "Phelps is not playing for small change," he cautioned. "If you trap him and expose him he stands to lose a business that is making him a fortune. There isn't much he would do, not even short of murder, to protect himself. Not much is known about how he got started—he had Andrew Johnson's patronage during the war, and he made money selling shoddy goods to the Army. Since then he has swung some big deals for railroad companies, oil companies—we know for certain he made at least a hundred thousand dollars from gas companies here in New York city for squashing a bill that would lower prices and cut their profits. So I'm asking you to do a dangerous thing."

No, anyone attempting to trap Mr. Phelps might easily find that this fox had sharp teeth.

At the Kenmore a page boy met her just inside the door.

"I'd like to see Mr. Edward Phelps, please."

His back stiffened just a little as he led her to the elevator. "Would you like to send up your card?" he asked.

"No. I'll just go up unannounced." She could tell this was not customary procedure, but then she probably wasn't the customary kind of visitor for Phelps. Since the boy was undecided as to what to do, she stepped firmly into the elevator, making up his mind for him.

At the next floor she followed the boy down the hall to Room 98. At their knock a man's voice told them to come in. Barely raising his head from his desk when he heard whom they wanted, the secretary called sharply, "Ed!"

"Tell her to come in here," ordered a man from the other room, and she was ushered in.

The sight of Phelps surprised her. From her own story in the *World*:

"Are you Mr. Phelps?" I asked, only to make him confess the fact.

"Yes, madam," he replied, smiling slightly, while he offered me a chair.

I sat down and looked about me. This was not what I had pictured to myself. This self-possessed, smiling man could not be the vampire I had been made to believe him. As he sat in the chair close by me with a reassuring smile on his face he did not look more than fifty-five years old. He is not a robust man, yet he is not of delicate build. There was nothing gaudy or loud about him, as one might imagine from his politics. His hair and his side whiskers are

[ 98 ]

gray. His upper lip and chin are clean shaven and he has something of the parson in his appearance.

The room in which we sat was comfortably furnished. It was apparently fitted up for an office.

I thought my surest bait for this occasion was assumed innocence and a natural ignorance—not entirely assumed—as to how such affairs are conducted.

"Mr. Phelps, I came to consult you on a matter of importance," I began nervously as if afraid of my position. "I—I hope no one can overhear us?" and I looked at him imploringly.

"Oh, no, you are safe to speak here," he assured me with a pleasant smile. He drew his chair closer . . . meanwhile looking me over critically.

She had brought with her the Smith Patent Medicine Bill, or rather a copy of it. This bill, introduced into a Senate committee, was soon to be brought out on the floor of the legislature for a vote, and if passed would practically eliminate the flood of quack remedies which were now selling profitably all over the state—to the injury of the health and the pocketbooks of the people.

It was a good bill, but Nellie, in the role of "Mrs. Brown," pretended to be against it. She told Phelps that her husband had a factory, a patent medicine factory, in Philadelphia, but they sold chiefly in the state of New York. Her husband was ill; she had come to New York to place some advertisements and had there learned of the bill. A friend had advised her to go to Albany to see Mr. Phelps.

Phelps nodded. He left the room, returned with a

ledger, turned to a page that was filled with all kinds of data on bills, nodded with satisfaction and closed the book.

Nellie plunged right in. "Do you think you could kill it?"

"Oh, yes," he responded heartily. "Never fear, I'll have it killed."

She should have been prepared. Nevertheless, his appearance, his gentlemanly ways, had disarmed her. She had begun to doubt he was what they said he was. Now, however, his blunt, matter-of-fact statement that he, Edward Phelps—one man—could kill the bill in the state legislature, that he had so much power he didn't even need to give it a second thought or wonder how it could be done—was like a shock of icy water thrown over her. It was true, then! This was not a democratic state run by the people through their elected representatives; it was a state owned and controlled by men like this one.

He had no suspicion of her, although he questioned her closely. Who had sent her? This she evaded, saying she could not give his name without his permission. What and where was her husband's factory? Never before had Nellie's ability as an actress come to such good purpose. To Phelps, she was just the kind of woman he liked to deal with: eager, naïve, unused to bargaining, the kind who might be the pillar of the church back home but quite willing to be dishonest among strangers.

Her story in the *World* continues:

". . . . it will take money, you know." Phelps said. It was a shock, this cool assertion. I clutched at my umbrella.

[ 100 ]

"I am willing to pay anything up to $2000," I said, faintly. "If you will assure me that it will be stopped."

"I can assure you that," he said, confidently. "Of course, you don't need to talk of $2000. You see, there will be my expenses, and then I will have to pay some Assemblymen."

He went to the end of the room and took from there some pages containing the names and classifications of Assemblymen and Senators—a list of committees. Under the title of "Affairs of Cities" he showed me the twelve committee names of the men who he said would kill or save the bill.

"Mr. Crosby of New York is a rich man, and can't be bought," he said calmly. "But we can buy Gallagher, of Erie; Tallmadge, of Kings; Prime, of Essex; De Witt, of Ulster; Hagan, of New York; and McLoughlin, of Kings. The rest are no good."

And as he mentioned each name he made a big, bold pencil check opposite each of their names. Nellie's heart gave a bound. This was her evidence! The fox had walked right into her trap!

"How much will it take for them?" I asked, innocently.

"You can get the lot for $1000."

"I must never be known to be connected with this," I said, beginning to cry. "It frightens me, I wouldn't have it known for anything. Though," I added, "I am willing to pay anything to have it killed."

"That is nothing," he said, lightly. "That is my

business. I just stay here to watch bills for railroad presidents, insurance companies, etc. I'm kept here just to do this. There is a lawyer by the name of Bates in New York who is also assisting me in getting people who want to fight the same bill you are here about. I've had my agents send out hundreds of copies of it."

So that was how it was done! And not only was Phelps an agent for certain companies, a lobbyist for them, but also he solicited business; he kept an eye on bills, figured to himself who would be interested in keeping or passing it, sent them copies of the bill—and then sat back and waited for them to beg his assistance.

In her mind's eye, she could see the whole network of evil practices spreading its invisible threads throughout the state, affecting the lives of every citizen.

Phelps made arrangements to meet "Mrs. Brown" at his office in New York on the following Friday to make final arrangements and to get her money.

She rose to go. "I'll take that list home to show my husband," she said, stretching out her hand for the marked copy of the senators who could be bought. But Phelps snatched it from her. He was too cunning.

"Give it to me!" he cried. "Your husband may know some of these men and may tell them." A lobbyist stayed in business only if he protected the names of the men he was dealing with, men who showed their respectable fronts to the public while their hands, in back of them, reached for Phelps's bribes. They had to trust him not to let them down.

Nellie's heart sank. Her only concrete evidence was

slipping right out of her hands. She begged him for the list "to show my husband." She knew so little of business—her husband might not believe her without this evidence—she might not get the money—her husband would want something more than her word, she really needed that list—

Phelps walked over to his desk, thinking deeply. He placed the paper down. "I'll tell you what I'll do. I'll cross them all out—check all the names. You can remember the ones I told you and show them to him. Then if this falls into anyone's hands, it won't mean a thing." He picked up the paper and pencil. Nellie watched him with an agony of apprehension. She wanted to grab it and run.

Then she saw something that made her want to shout with joy. Phelps *had* picked up the paper, laid it down and made a check, but not on the desk! It was on a *rough-textured, coarse-grained, pebbly-covered book,* and the pencil marks he made down the page, checking opposite all the rest of the names, were very, very different from the six pencil marks he had made for the six he could buy. The new marks came through in dotted fashion; the others, the first ones, were smooth and clear and straight.

Afraid that he might change his mind again, yet afraid to show her eagerness, she went through the painful torment of saying good-bye, repeating where and when they would meet in New York, but once she was out of the room she nearly ran all the way to the Stanwix, the incriminating paper safe in her big clasp purse. There she made memorandums of all the pertinent facts of the interview, and all the exact, verbatim memorizing she had done of the actual things Phelps had said. She had a feeling she was going to need a clear memory and unassailable proof, once her story was printed.

But it was not to be written yet.

There was still the other meeting to come first. And this next interview in Phelps's office brought her perilously close to being exposed. His son was the only other person present. Phelps, now that he was sure of his victim and could look forward to getting his money, was genial and relaxed and in a boasting mood. He told her the bill had been killed and she had nothing more to worry about.

He made some extremely damaging statements:

"So soon? How clever you must be!" I remarked flatteringly. "How did you ever manage it?" I asked, with a world of admiration in my eyes.

"Why, you see . . ." he talked in a confiding whisper. "I went to work on it right away. You see I had it transferred from the Committee that first had it. As I told you, Mr. Crosby could not be bought, and I saw he and some others were determined to pass it, so I went to the ones I told you I could get and told them I wanted that bill killed. . . ."

"They did not dare refuse," I murmured.

"No, I should say they did not," he said laughingly. "You see, that's my business. I'm the head of the Lobby. . . . I keep a lot of runners who watch and know everything that happens. They report to me and I have books in my rooms where entries are made of every bill and notes of every incident connected with it. . . ."

"Then you can have any bill killed?"

"I have control of the House and can pass or kill any bill that so pleases me," was Mr. Phelps astounding reply.

It wasn't just a boast, she knew that. He meant it. This was big business. They might call him a fox and it was true he had the cunning of one. But to her he was more like a spider, a poisonous one, silent, stealthy, loathsome.

Phelps asked her for a check—one thousand dollars for the men he had bought off and two hundred and fifty for himself. He explained that he was making the sum for himself so small because there were others besides herself who had been interested in having the bill killed. It was safe to guess that they had paid him, too, and paid plenty.

Nellie stalled. In her anxiety to get this story she had forgotten to think carefully through this part of it. What could she do? She had no intention of paying in cash. But neither did she want to write a forged check with the name of Nellie Brown on it. She explained that her husband had warned her not have their names involved in this, because they were afraid they might get caught. She couldn't write a check.

"Very well," said Phelps. "My son will go with you to your hotel and you can pay him in cash."

This wouldn't do, either She was not stopping at any hotel. If the son went with her she would be exposed immediately. And if she gave a check here, Phelps would know in fifteen minutes, at the bank, that she was a fake. Even though her story would come out tomorrow, he would have today and tomorrow to cover up his traces and warn the others.

There was just one way out. It was not only a way out, but her imagination, lightning quick, saw a new trap for Phelps in it.

She argued. She did not want the son to go with her.

Phelps's eyes grew a cold as bullets. Now she saw him as ruthless and as terrifying as he really was, all the genial, gentlemanly surface gone. He still had no suspicions of who she was, but he evidently thought she was trying to get out of paying him. As Nellie looked at that hard, tight mouth she felt sorry for anyone, any ordinary person, who might try to cheat this man. He was dangerous, menacing.

But still she pleaded: "Please, Mr. Phelps, why can't *you* come with me to the hotel? I hate to have your son connected with this. It's just one more person who knows about it and my husband will be furious. Besides, I am better acquainted with you." She pretended to be coquettish.

It worked. He finally, angrily, agreed.

This was what she wanted, but she was still in danger. It all depended on how fast she worked, how fast she moved, so as to leave him no time to think! As they came out of the office building she saw a cab, walked with the unsuspecting Phelps up to it, then swiftly she sprang into it, saying to the startled lobby king: "I can't be seen with you on the streets, Mr. Phelps. I'll take one cab and you take another." Before he could protest she was gone, urging the cabby to whip up his horses. The carriage disappeared around the corner before the amazed Phelps could gather his wits.

Nellie made the cab driver go by twists and turns. Then, when she was sure she wasn't being followed, she directed him to the *World* office. Now for the rest of her plan. She had told Phelps the name of the hotel; she was sure he would go there. Quickly she sent another reporter to the St. James Hotel to watch for him. This would be one more person to verify her story, one more pair of eyes to see that Edward Phelps had really come to collect his money.

The reporter confirmed: hidden by a pillar he had watched as the lobbyist paced the hotel waiting room. He saw Phelps become impatient, worried, angry. A messenger was sent and presently the son arrived. There was a heated consultation; the son timidly peeked into the Ladies' Parlor, returned to shake his head in denial. Phelps was seen to clap his hat on his head angrily and leave, appointing his son to stay and keep watch. Soon the father returned and they both went out to the street corner to wait a few moments. Another *World* reporter, posted across the street at the Delmonico Restaurant, watched their growing discomfiture. Just to make absolutely sure of his facts, he walked across and spoke to Phelps, calling him by name. By three o'clock both father and son were seen to give up their vigil and walk away, very worried men.

They needed to be.

The *World* headlined Nellie's story on the front page the next day.

### THE KING OF THE LOBBY

#### EDWARD R. PHELPS CAUGHT IN A NEATLY LAID TRAP

#### NELLIE BLY'S INTERESTING EXPERIENCES IN ALBANY

There was a cartoon drawing of Phelps, a crown on his head, his feet up on a desk, his chair surrounded by bags of money. A *World* poet had contributed a jingle beneath the drawing:

> "For I'm a Pirate King!
>     I'm in the Lobby Ring;
> Oh, what an uproarious, Jolly and Glorious
>     Biz for a Pirate King!"

And Nellie's story started with:

I was a lobbyist last week. I went up to Albany to catch a professional briber in the act. I did so. The briber, lobbyist and boodler whom I caught was Mr. Ed Phelps. . . .

and went on to tell the story, dramatically, column after column of the actual conversation that had taken place, both in Albany and in New York. Not one person reading that story could have doubted the truth and the authenticity of it.

The whole state of New York was in an uproar over the story. It burst like a bombshell. The next day the *World* carried a long story of Phelps's denial, printing it without comment, letting his own tortuous, weaseling explanations get him in deeper and deeper until no one could possibly believe him.

Copies of those issues of the *World* quickly sold out. Special editions were printed. The story of how a girl named Nellie Bly had caught the cleverest of lobbyists was on everyone's lips, not only in New York and Albany, but in the whole state as well. Many were the long conferences in smoke-filled rooms where men who had

had dealings with Phelps frantically tried to figure out their own salvation. The public demanded an investigation. The legislature was bombarded with letters and delegations from furious citizens, determined to see that this corruption was wiped out, or at least brought out into the light of day.

Nellie was hailed as a heroine. The impudence of a young woman braving the fox in his own den—and trapping him—appealed hugely to the imagination of people. She was their own, their champion. They read her story and passed it from hand to hand, examining in detail the picture the *World* had printed of that very page with the two distinct kinds of pencil markings. So the men they had elected from their own district—Tallmadge of Kings, Prime of Essex and Gallagher of Erie—men like that could be bought for as little as a thousand dollars! And Phelps bragging that he could kill or save any bill he chose to—what did this mean to them, the people of New York State? It meant their lives, their affairs, their wages and their businesses were in the hands of crooks.

The State Senate soon realized they could not escape this public pressure; there would have to be an investigation.

The *World* hammered away at them every day. Every day there was another story. One of them was headed "A Bomb in the Legislature." This was an account of the day that the six men bought by Phelps rose to their feet to make their denials, some of them belligerent, some pathetic, some blustering, some self-righteously demanding that their good names be cleared.

On the next Thursday, therefore, Cockerill was able

to print the news that the Lobby King had been at last arraigned by a special senatorial committee to investigate the story and his practices. Unfortunately, the news was not quite exact: the investigating committee, fearful of more exposures, limited the arraignment only to finding out the truth of Nellie's story and not to any digging into lobby practices.

Nellie was called to the witness stand.

(Special to the *World*) Albany, April 18—

The sensation of the day in Albany was the appearance before the House Judiciary Committee, of the bright young correspondent of the *World*, who so neatly entrapped the shrewd old lobbyist, Edward R. Phelps, into betraying the secrets of his profession. For the past two weeks, the greatest curiosity has existed in Albany to see her. Many country papers declared that Nellie Bly was a myth and that the stories were prepared in the *World* office. But Nellie Bly was there, and so was a vast crowd, including scores of Albany women.

The story went on:

The entire committee was also there. Many Senators and Congressmen were drawn there out of curiosity. Gen. James William Husted, who mutilated the resolution to such an extent as practically to destroy its value, was also there, chuckling at the impotency of the committee's efforts in sifting the lobby business to the bottom.

When Chairman Saxton announced that the committee could only confine itself to that part of Nellie

Bly's story that related to Phelps's boast that he could buy Messrs. Gallagher . . . Tallmadge . . . Prime . . . DeWitt . . . Hagan . . . and McLoughlin . . . the weakness and worthlessness of the resolution was fully apparent.

## NELLIE BLY APPEARS

The committee waited until 4 o'clock for Mr. Phelps to appear. He did not and Nellie Bly, who had been sitting in the room of Col. McEwan, acting Adjutant-General, took the stand. She fully sustained every detail in the interview she had with Phelps and which was published in the *World* on April 1. Her answers were clear, direct, straightforward and uttered with a naïvete that captivated the audience.

After she was finished there was not the slightest doubt in the minds of all honest men of the accuracy of her statements and the truth. A sensation was produced when Edwards Phelps, pale and trembling with excitement, rose from a chair at the foot of the table, where he had come without being noticed, and, pointing his finger at the witness, who was perfectly cool and self-possessed, asked: "Did I say buy? Did I say *buy*?"

Nothing Phelps could do or say could hide the truth from that audience—or from the readers of any newspaper in the state. It was true, as the *World* had bitterly said, that the sting had been taken out of the investigation when it confined itself only to Nellie's story and not to lobbying in general. But just the same the effect of her story and the indignation of the public had had its effect.

Nellie had a visit from a man named Dr. Parkhurst. She had heard of him, and of the group of public-spirited, decent men who acted with him, in connection with his long fight to get rid of the grafters in the city of New York. He had aimed his sights at the boss of them all—Boss Tweed—and had succeeded in getting him put in jail. He was still carrying on a relentless fight to purge both city and state of rotten politicians.

Now he said:

"You are an inspiration to us all, young lady. Now, with what you have done in opening up this rotten situation, members of my committee can carry on. We have them on the run and I promise you we won't give up until we break up these lobby gangs."

Not as pleasant as that one had been another interview.

Cockerill had called her to his office just before she was to appear in the House.

"I'm putting a bodyguard on you," he said, crisply. "No, don't argue. It would be worth a great deal to those men to keep you from appearing on the stand tomorrow. And Nellie, for Heaven's sake, get some rest. You look tired. You don't look very excited for a young lady who is the talk of the town."

"I am tired," she said passing a hand over her eyes.

He walked around his desk and stood with a fatherly arm around her shoulders. "Nellie, we ask a lot of you. It's your own fault, too—this is the kind of thing you wanted to do. But I think I may have made a mistake in giving you this Phelps story."

[ 112 ]

"Why? I did the job. Do you think it could have been done better?"

"No—no. It's not that. It's just—well, the men on the staff are pretty sore about it. They don't feel this was a woman's story. They don't think a woman should be meddling in things that concern politics and crime. I'm afraid I've let you in for some pretty rough handling—there's a lot of jealousy and a lot of hurt feelings and some of the men were in here with a delegation to see me. They want to make sure you stay in your own pastures and don't stray into their field."

This was a deep cup of bitterness for Nellie to drink.

# 7

The gay, merry pleasure times were over.

What Cockerill said was only too true. As a body, the reporters of the *World* disapproved of a woman getting mixed up in the slimy business of lobby politics. They were furious; they were disgusted with Nellie herself. She had no business stepping out of a woman's place. Partly it was jealousy, because this was indeed a journalistic scoop of the first degree, and some felt they had been cheated of their chance at it.

Inside the office she was treated with distant coolness; outside, she was no longer their friend and companion.

Nellie reacted with even more coolness. This helped to build higher the wall around her. If she had been less independent, yes, less arrogant and suspicious, she might have seen that some of these men had a legitimate complaint: they were *World* veterans of the newspaper field and felt they had a right to be considered on a story as big as that of Phelps's. But she couldn't see it.

Quite rightly, she felt that their comradeship with her permitted her, a woman, just a glimpse inside the door. They had not really admitted her to full equality with them.

[ 114 ]

Even when one or two, ashamed, tried once more to be friends, she refused them. Even when invitations came from acquaintances and friends, like Metcalf, from outside the *World*, she no longer believed them to be genuine. She said no. And she had the excuse that her mother had come to live with her so that what free time she had must be spent in finding a larger apartment and settling them both in it.

It was lucky for her emotional state that she had very little free time.

Cockerill plunged her into work.

Now she really began to cover New York. Now she was again doing her own kind of stories. As she had in Pittsburgh, she went into tenement districts, into slums, into all the places where the poor of the city lived. She found disease, to the point of being epidemic, in the congested areas of the city. Picking up her long skirts and holding her nose, she even ventured into the alleyways— alleys that had no names but where people lived in tumble-down shacks, in mud and filth and dirt and garbage. As far as the city was concerned, these alleys didn't exist. There was no sanitation provided for them, no garbage collected, no gas lights, no heat. These people were the forgotten, the despised, the very poor.

But Nellie caused them to be remembered again. She shoved them and their conditions under the haughty noses of the city fathers. As a result, civic leaders, clutching copies of her articles, toured the worst of them. They came out stunned and horrified.

Her stories forced New York to look at its tenements, too: a picture of apartment dwellings where a single faucet in a hallway served ten or twelve families for drinking and cooking and bathing water; where the outside toilets were filthy and fly encrusted; where rats as big as cats terrorized the children and defied the adults.

Through Nellie, the *World* made demands for better housing, better sanitation, more visiting doctors to the poor. And they had some measure of success. Investigations were held and laws were tightened up, some even enforced.

Immigrants were pouring in from Europe. They had been led to believe that America had gold on the streets, to be picked up for the asking. They thought they had come to the end of poverty, of exploitation, of crooked politicians and of hard landlords. America, whose plants and factories were mushrooming up to fantastic growths such as the world had never seen before, needed their labor. Agents were sent abroad to tempt the workers to the New World.

The immigrants woke from their dreams to find themselves in slums and in ghetto-like conditions hardly better than those they had left. They spoke little English. They were confused and bewildered, easy to prey upon and easy to cheat.

These were the things Nellie saw and wrote about.

She investigated employment agencies, finding some of them to be out-and-out frauds. Posing as an immigrant girl looking for work, she learned that these agencies took her money in advance, promised her jobs and then sent her, knowingly, to places where there was no work. Or when she asked for a job as a servant, they placed her right away—in a home where she had to carry buckets of coal up four flights of stairs, where the basement kitchen was big and old, where water had to be pumped from a well—and where she was literally on her feet and working for fourteen hours a day. When she indignantly reported back to the agency, they just shrugged her off. Other girls, wiser than she, told her that the same agency sent girl after girl to that same house—collecting the fee each time.

Again, as in Pittsburgh, she went into factories. But now she worked in them: a box factory, a pottery. She did not find the work too hard, but there was a surprise in store for Nellie.

At the box factory, especially, she met and talked to girls who were different than any she had met before. They were fighting back, unsatisfied with their conditions, unwilling to take abuse from foremen or put up with the low wages, the poor lighting and the long hours.

"We won't put up with it any longer," they told her. "Haven't you heard what happened up at Lowell, Massachusetts? The girls went out on strike there—they marched in the streets!"

"But"—Nellie was horrified—"those girls were set upon by a mob. Some of them were hurt. You can't do things that way."

"We don't want to—not if we can help it. But things are changing. I had a friend who worked up there. Why, the owner of the mills thought he owned those girls, body and soul. He told them where they had to live, how late they could stay out at night, what kind of friends they could have, what books they could read. He had his spies—every landlady in his rooming houses told him if a girl stayed out after ten o'clock and who her boy friend was. And if it didn't suit His Majesty, then the girl got fired. Haven't you heard that song the girls sing:

"As we come marching, marching—
We battle, too, for men.
For they are women's children and we mother them,
    again.
Our lives shall not be sweated from birth until life
    closes—
Hearts can starve as well as bodies,
Give us bread—and give us roses!"

It was through her co-workers in the box factory that
Nellie was invited to Pythagoras Hall.

"It's a secret meeting, mind you," she was told. "Not
a word of it must go out. We're very careful who we let
come in." If they had known they were talking to a reporter for the *World*!

On the night of the meeting Nellie walked the six
blocks from her apartment to Pythagoras Hall. Her first
impulse had been to engage a hansom cab, as she did
usually at night, but then she realized that the other girls
would be suspicious of anyone throwing away money
like that.

By twos and three, quietly, almost secretly, the girls
slipped in through the doors of the hall. Women guards
were stationed at each door. The big hall was crowded;
girls called to friends, laughed or gathered in little knots
for serious talk.

All this stopped when the meeting was called to order.

"Girls," called a slim, middle-aged woman on the platform, "let's get down to business. I was elected temporary
chairman at our last meeting and if I don't know all the
rules of how to conduct a meeting, then you will just have
to overlook it because I've never done anything like this

[ 118 ]

before. First, we are going to hear a report from our sisters who work at Wallach's Department Store."

A girl got up. She started out shy and uncertain of herself, but soon she was speaking freely, carried away by what she was saying.

". . . and we have no place to eat our lunches in except the basement, and that's full of boxes and people running all around us packing and sorting and yelling at us to get out of their way. No chairs to sit down on, even."

Another, older, woman got to her feet. "We had the same trouble at our place. But we asked the men to help us. So they went to the boss and told him we were getting in their way and they couldn't work like that. So we got an empty storeroom to ourselves and some of the men helped to make us some chairs and a table." She sat down quickly, blushing as if she were surprised at her own daring in getting up at a meeting to speak.

Then the chairman made a little speech. "We women have to get together," she began. "The men have unions. If we organize ourselves we, too, will have strength. Then we can demand better things for ourselves."

This touched off a wave of applause and a chorus of *no's*! Argument raged back and forth, and finally to put an end to it the chairman announced they had a special speaker for the evening—a woman much interested in social welfare, a civic-minded, wealthy woman who had come to address them.

"I have heard some of your stories of your wrongs and I have listened to your attempts to find solutions," she said. "But I think you are making a greater mistake yet—and that is in seeking work in the shops and stores and factories. I beg you to return to what is woman's natural place—the home. It used to be that women who needed to support themselves by their own efforts became, as a matter of course, the 'hired help' in other women's houses. Their mistresses were kind and benevolent; they were treated as members of the family; they ate at the same table as the family. The mistress took an interest in what they did, even in the clothes they wore. The mistress saw to it that they went to church, supervised their education and their amusements. When they married, the mistress usually had a hand in helping them make their choice and they were married from the very home in which they had worked. They were protected and sheltered and cared for. What has happened to these Mehitabels and Abigails? Now you find them working at machines or over store counters. They are thrust into a rude world where their womanly standards are coarsened by daily contact with men of business. They can be fired at any minute and left stranded and penniless, and they are exposed to all the vices of a big city; there is no one to supervise their spiritual life. I beg you women to think of what I am saying—there is a great need for domestic service and you will be welcomed back to where you rightfully belong."

The speaker sat down. But she hardly had time to adjust her furs and straighten her hat before the storm broke around her.

Nellie's friend was the first on her feet.

"I used to be one of those Abigails you talk about. My mistress was neither kind nor benevolent and the happiest moment of my life was when I could tell her I was leaving. And the second happiest moment was when I had my first pay check at the factory; I went right out and bought myself a dress. Then I took that faded, patched garment my mistress had so 'kindly' given me and I flung it right in her face. Who wants to be treated as one of the family, if you are the one that does all the work, gets all the abuse, eats the poorest food?"

"Working in a store may be hard work," interrupted another, "but at least I can call my soul my own. No one is prying into everything I think and everything I do. Nobody is telling me I must go to church service on my only evening off, whether I feel up to it or not."

Another voice cried from the rear of the room: "Marriage! My mistress did everything she could to keep me from getting married. She didn't want to lose me—not she—too fat and lazy to do her own work!"

Laughter swept the hall, breaking the tension. The chairman signaled for order; behind her back the guest speaker's face was purple with indignation.

A very young and very pretty girl timidly took the floor. She spoke in such a shy, low voice she could hardly be heard. "It's true there are many things in a big city that shock me," she admitted. "But it—it is easier to be a—a *good* girl here where there are so many people surrounding you—and you work in a public way—than it is in a home. I was always being bothered"—she colored up to the roots of her hair—"by my master and his sons."

At the end of the meeting another reminder came from the chairman for secrecy. They must prevent any word of the meeting from leaking out; if employers knew the names of women who attended they might easily lose their jobs.

In her room that night, for just a moment Nellie struggled with conscience. She was a reporter and this was her story. But did she have the right to tell what happened at Pythagoras Hall? Was it a betrayal of those women? She was confused, torn between two loyalties. This choice had never been forced upon her before; when she wrote of the factories and streets she was helping the people of whom she wrote. Now what was she to do?

It was only a moment. She was, first and foremost, a newspaper woman. Her choice lay with her job.

The next week, as she again came to the meeting hall, her story—unsigned—was a principal topic.

"Is there a traitor here again tonight?" the chairman demanded to know. "Is one of us, a workingwoman, the author of the story in the *World*?"

A few protested that the publicity might do no harm, might even help their cause. The writer of the article had not mentioned names. But these voices were drowned out. The women were rightfully afraid of any leak that might lead to their dismissal; employers did not look with any favor upon women who banded together for their mutual assistance—troublemakers, they were called.

Sitting quietly and inconspicuously in the audience, Nellie heard herself called a "traitor" and the word stung like a whip. It was a shock to her, worse than anything she had experienced, because she was accustomed to something so very different from workingwomen. She was used to being called a friend to the poor, a champion of the worker, a woman to whom other women turned to for the righting of their wrongs. She was hurt, furious, uncomfortably unsure of the justice or injustice of the name—*traitor*!

After the meeting she was taken aside. For a second she was uneasy. Did they suspect? But it was for a far different matter . . . she was asked to *join* the society as a sister, to work with them for their mutual betterment, to pledge her honor in keeping their names, their purpose and their meetings sacred and secret.

Shame and guilt, embarrassment—and a desire to laugh—made Nellie mumble and stutter in her refusal. She was sorry, she couldn't do it, she was leaving the box factory, she was going home to her sister in Maine, she was sorry—

And finally she escaped. But this story would be her last on the meetings at the hall. Even if she could have continued to fool the other women, she had lost all desire to do so. The story had left a bad taste in her mouth and an unhappy sensation of being on the wrong side of the situation for once.

It was a relief to be back at her desk in the *World*. The mail was pouring in, appealing to Nellie Bly for assistance. Her wounded feelings were eased. The letters begged: "Help us! Write about us, Nellie Bly! We are cheated—we are poor—we are preyed upon—help us!"

Her search for her exposé stories led her on strange journeys.

Once she visited the dispensaries for the poor where, for ten cents each, prescriptions could be obtained and where the doctors treated the sick without charge. Nellie's conclusions were that New York's dispensaries were administered with genuine concern for the pockets of the poor, that there was not enough appreciation given for this work, that as charity it was good charity. But she was shocked that they permitted young doctors without adequate training to work there just to get the experience—experimenting on the poor who could not object. As she waited in the hallway for her turn she could hear a woman screaming while a doctor took out her tonsils. In addition to the tonsil infection, the woman was suspected of having cancer of the throat.

Then it was Nellie's turn. She described it for the *World*:

> I sat down facing him [the doctor] and glanced about; the walls were covered with pictures of the throat, in all conditions. . . .
>
> "What is wrong?" he asked curtly, taking my book and glancing through it.
>
> "My throat," I replied, with ebbing spirits.
>
> "Let me see," he said, taking a small instrument out of a finger bowl. "Open your mouth wide."
>
> I opened it. I did not want to, but I knew I was in for it. He caught my chin firmly and ran the instrument down by throat. Just then the horrible thought came to me that with that same thing he had looked into the other woman's throat. *And she had cancer!*

It was for courage like that, courage that led her to risk her health, her life and safety to get her stories—for that people loved her, honored her, jeered at her; but no matter how they felt they read her.

The joke had gone round the city: "Don't hire that girl, she might be Nellie Bly!" She was never caught in any of her masquerades, but she came very close to it. Only her ability as an actress saved her.

On one such occasion she undertook the job of trapping a man who sought out and tricked lonely, simple country girls into lives of prostitution.

Her story "The Infamy of the Park" was so horrifying that it almost sounded like fiction, except that it was true. She verified it in detail. If it took courage for her to get the story, it also took courage on the part of the *World* to print it, because she unhesitatingly named the police as being in full knowledge and support of the man's vile practices.

Cockerill and Pulitzer had come to know that Nellie never "puffed up" a story. When she gave them facts they could depend on them to be true. So for this story they risked lawsuits and slander suits.

Even so, when this headline appeared the legal department of the paper held its breath:

## THE INFAMY OF THE PARK

### Nellie Bly Unearths a Scoundrel Favored by Police

Charles Cleveland, a man of leisure, debauches Central Park to his own vileness. . . . He drives there daily and invites young girls to ride—the police smile at him and assist in getting his prey. . . .

If it had not been true, it was indeed a bold charge to make against the police. The fact that her story was not denied by the officers involved was proof enough for New Yorkers.

One day a letter came to Nellie from a woman who had noticed a peculiar happening that afternoon in Central Park. A man had driven his carriage up and down the lanes, finally stopping to persuade a young girl to take a ride with him. Coming back from the ride, the girl was badly frightened and ran away as soon as she could get out of the carriage. The woman caught up with her and found her almost too scared to speak, but she finally admitted that the man had tried to talk her into going into the country with him. He had boasted that the police helped him, solicited girls for him and for the woman who owned the team of horses he drove.

"Nellie Bly," the letter urged, "this man is dangerous. Can't you find out something about him?"

Nellie dressed herself as a simple country girl, in a flowered cotton, faded but clean. She covered the tight bodice with an old pink shawl and wore a straw hat with big roses on it.

She walked slowly through the drive, pausing often to look about her as a stranger would. Then she sat on a bench that faced the drive that led from Fifty-ninth Street to Seventy-second. She had not long to wait.

An open carriage was circling, circling, driving slower and coming nearer each time. Other cabs passed, but this one kept coming back every few minutes. Nellie raised her eyes from her book. She was right; this was the man. He was beckoning to her smilingly, inviting her to ride with him. She looked away just in time to see a police guard exchange a knowing wink and a smile with the man in the carriage.

She got up and walked on, but the carriage followed her. She stopped and so did he. This time he got out to speak to an older woman who seemed to be waiting for him at the turn. As Nellie turned back, the woman left hurriedly and the man planted himself solidly in Nellie's path.

"How about a little ride, girlie?" he asked. His voice was rough and coarse. "It's a swell day for a drive and I have good horses. Come on, let's have some fun!"

She let herself be coaxed, blushing and keeping her eyes on the ground. But when she was seated in the carriage, she asked "Aren't you afraid to be doing this?"

"Why?"

"The policemen. Won't they arrest you for picking up girls?"

He laughed. "Not me. We understand each other. I buy them a few beers and they just look the other way. In fact, they point out little girls like you to me. If girls make any trouble they'd be more likely to arrest them than me."

She asked him his name. He was cautious. "Oh, just call me Charles."

"And the name of the woman you were speaking to?"

"She's a friend of mine. She owns these horses. She keeps a place—a roadhouse up on 116th Street."

While he boasted of how he could get her, a simple little country girl, on the stage because of his close acquaintance with prominent theater managers, she had a chance to observe him. He wore a linen duster buttoned up to his chin, but where the collar peeped over it she could see that it was soiled. His chin was covered with a stubble of whiskers, his mustache long and drooping, his hair growing low over his forehead. Whatever success he had with women could not be due to his good looks. She felt that poor, lonely girls, cut off from fun and social life because they had no money and were strangers in the city, would be his prey. They might consider his coarse manner friendly and jolly.

He was also shrewd in not pressing his advantage that first day. He brought her straight back to the bench where he had first seen her.

"Tomorrow?" he asked.

"I can't," she said coyly. "But I'll be here the day after."

The next day Nellie stayed out of sight, but she posted a photographer along the man's usual haunts to get a picture, and asked another reporter to find out what he could of Mr. Charles's woman friend.

The photographer got his picture of Mr. Charles. The other reporter, grabbing a hansom cab, followed the carriage to a livery stable, where he was able to learn that Charles was the man's first name—Charles Cleveland; that he was a foreman of the stable and the horses were actually the property of a respectable judge who was vacationing and knew nothing of Charles's borrowing them. And he learned, too, that Cleveland had a bad reputation, of which he freely boasted.

The next day Nellie was back in the park.

She wasn't afraid even after she was in the carriage, though today she noticed a change in Charles's manner. He had smartened and cleaned himself up a little, and had dropped the good, friendly pal role. Blustering and bossy, he paid no attention to Nellie's objections; they were going to the roadhouse that belonged to his friend.

At 116th Street he stopped before a one-story frame house, threw the reins to a boy who had come up from the basement areaway and who seemed to know the team and its master well. Again she noticed Cleveland raise his hand in a familiar, joking salute to two mounted policemen, who acknowledged it with careless, knowing waves of their hands.

Then he pushed Nellie into the house ahead of him.

She should have been frightened. As far as she could tell, except for the murmur of a woman's voice from the kitchen, she was alone with Cleveland. Should she run now? No, she wanted her story. What was there to tell, up to now, except that a man had offered her a ride and brought her to an unpleasant house? But in spite of that, her nerves tightened.

He brought back two drinks. He had combed his hair and straightened his collar to make himself look dashing, and was evidently quite proud of himself.

"But this doesn't look like lemonade, to me," she protested.

"I put a little sherry in it. What's the matter? Go on and drink it. Do you think I put some kind of drug in it?"

Something in his voice told her the drink had something in it much more alcoholic than sherry. She was alone with Cleveland; no one from the *World* knew where she was or could help her—and a drugged drink would put her at his mercy.

"I don't want it."

He raised his big, beefy hand and pushed her into a chair.

"What's the matter with you? I told you I'd see you had a good time. I'm going to a summer resort soon and I'll take you with me. And I spoke to some theater managers I told you about and they'd like to hear you sing. Go on, sing for me. There's a piano. I want to hear you sing."

Nellie was furious. "I don't intend to sing. And I want to be driven back to the park."

"Then drink your lemonade first," he ordered, cursing under his breath. "Go on; I have to pay for it. Are you afraid?"

"Yes, I am. I'd be afraid of any man who treated me as you do."

"What do you mean? I've treated you better than most men would," he hurled at her. "When girls act like you, most men would just throw them out and let them get back to town the best way they could."

But Nellie had caught an undertone of fear in his voice. The man was a bully, but he was also a coward. He was afraid of anyone who stood up to him. She took advantage of this and rose to go, facing him determinedly.

"I should think you'd get into trouble, going around picking up girls like this."

"Not me. It's the girls who get into trouble. And if I have any fuss with them I tip off the police and the girls get hauled in—to jail."

She was so shocked she could hardly speak. "You mean girls—that I myself—might get put in jail if I don't do what you ask?"

Cleveland laughed. "I know what I'm doing. I never ask regulars, the girls who know the city. I watch for strangers. I knew you were a stranger when I first saw you. I drive in that park all the time and I know when a strange girl comes into it."

She had what she had come for—proof from his own lips that he hunted women as a wolf hunts his prey. Even though her heart was hammering she made herself say, firmly: "Now, I want to be taken right back where you found me. And if you try to get me into any trouble, you'll find you've picked the wrong girl. I'm not as friendless as you seem to think."

Their eyes locked in silent battle for a second. She had been right; he was a coward. His face reddened and his eyes dropped. Without another word he led the way out to the street, helped her into the carriage and drove her back to the park.

She was safe. But how many other girls, gullible, lonely, frightened, weak girls, girls from whom he had nothing to fear—how many of them had he led to lives of shame and ruin? Nellie was so angry that her story the next day fairly spat with fury. It ran for three long columns.

New York was shocked. Alarm ran like a prairie fire through the police department. There was a shake-up and certain members of the force were suspended. Charles Cleveland himself vanished overnight. He was never seen in the park again.

But Nellie's fame spread.

Cockerill began to use her as a traveling correspondent for the *World*. He sent her to Washington to interview the wives of President Harrison's cabinet members. She was received in an interview with Mrs. Ulysses S. Grant and at another time with the poet, James Whitcomb Riley. She interviewed Belva Lockwood, the candidate for president on the Woman Suffrage ticket.

This assignment began as an ordinary reporting job, but it ended in a way that Nellie had not expected.

Belva Lockwood was running on the platform of Equal Rights:

We, the undersigned, citizens of the State of New York, believe in women suffrage, prohibition, arbitration, money and labor reform, and the control of railroads and telegraphs by the Government.

Oddly enough, this was Nellie's first official contact with the suffrage movement; odd, because the political-minded women leaders of the country had already hailed her as an outstanding example of what a woman could do if given the chance. Just as they had heard of her, she had heard of them. But her feelings were mixed. What kind of women were these who marched in parades, who worked persistently for years for votes for women, who had suffered indignity at the hands of mobs—were manhandled, had garbage thrown at them, been hauled into jails—what were they really like? Freaks? Strange, mannish creatures?

She was greatly surprised.

From her own account of the interview she gives her impression:

Mrs. Lockwood does not look like the cuts newspapers have published of her, still less does she answer to descriptions of her. She is a womanly woman; what greater praise can one give her? She is firm and intelligent without being manly; and gentle and womanly without being frivolous. She is the beau ideal of a woman with a brain. Six large diamonds, set in a square, caught a webby lace scarf about her throat, and from the coils of gray hair glistened a diamond comb. Her curly bang allows a space of broad forehead to show between it and her sparkling brown eyes. A few pinks and sprigs of mignonette were pinned close to her throat.

She questioned Mrs. Lockwood about her program. "What class of women support you in your Equal Rights program?"

"Thinking women and working women. Society women never go outside society," she answered quickly, smiling.

"I suppose you depend entirely on the vote of men to put you in office?"

"Certainly. Women have no vote," she replied. "We are coming to it, though. It is the universal opinion of all thinking men that women will eventually vote. I have been nominated as delegate to the Union Labor party and expected to leave for Cincinnati on the very day I was notified of my nomination for president."

They discussed her views on tariffs, on international arbitration of disputes, on immigration and the chances of her rival candidates.

The interview was over. To Nellie's surprise, Mrs. Lockwood turned the tables and became the questioner, asking all sorts of personal, intimate things about Nellie's life.

The answers appalled Mrs. Lockwood. "You mean you have no friends? You just work, go home, eat, sleep—and then work some more? You're too young for that, child. It is an unnatural life."

"Evidently, mine is an unnatural occupation," agreed Nellie bitterly.

"That is true. All the more reason why you should join with people who feel and think as you do. Why not join us, Nellie? Be with women—intelligent, thoughtful women who are fighting for what they believe. We have much to offer each other. I know; my husband was an invalid for fifteen years. I taught school during that time. It was poor pay and long hours. I tried everything else to make extra money—I even went out and did house-work, scrubbing floors. Finally I decided to study law and I did it at night. In 1873 I was admitted to the bar, a real lawyer. Then I found the suffrage movement. And life opened up for me, Nellie. I wasn't alone any more."

As always when forced to face a problem, Nellie paced up and down the floor. "I'll be as blunt as you have, Mrs. Lockwood. I'd be afraid to join. My position is difficult enough as it is; if I were to become a suffragist, that would be the weapon I'd put into the hands of my enemies. They would laugh at me. They may not like me now, but they don't laugh. They respect me."

The older woman shook her head. "Men aren't your enemies, Nellie. Ideas and prejudices are what we are fighting. I hope you will be as lucky as I was in my hus-band, and find a young man who is understanding and who will help you."

The girl exploded. "Help me? No one has ever helped me! Everything I've done, I've done by myself. No one has ever done anything for me."

"You must be wrong. It isn't possible for anyone to go through life and succeed without help from others. We are social human beings, not hermits. Are you sure, my dear, that it isn't you who are turning away from people?"

Nellie was thinking of the treatment she had received from the staff of the *World* after the Phelps story. It was a shock to realize how much and how deeply it had hurt her, though she had tried to pretend it hadn't and cov-

[ 134 ]

ered it up with indifference. Was Mrs. Lockwood right—
had she, too, been partly responsible for the rift? Could
she have won them over? And what about men like
Metcalf, who had tried in vain to see her?

"I think," she replied, still angry, "that young men
are afraid of me. I compete with them. What they want
is some soft creature who will look up to them and obey
them, who'd be afraid to walk down Park Row without
an escort, much less go where I do—into slums, alone."
She continued, thoughtfully, "I believe the only men
who have ever helped me have been much older men."

"That's probably true, what you said about the feeling
of competition. But believe me, if you think you don't
need people, you're wrong, Nellie! You're wrong!"

For weeks afterward Mrs. Lockwood's warning—
*"You're wrong, Nellie!"*—echoed in her mind. Was she
wrong not to join with these suffragist women? Had she
been wrong when she refused to join the group who met
in Pythagoras Hall? Had it been partly her fault that she
was almost cut off from the companionship of other
newspaper people?

Her mother seemed to think so, although she put it in
different words.

"Aren't you ever going to think of getting married,
Nellie? And how can you find anyone if you won't make
friends?" Mrs. Cochrane had adjusted well to New York.
She was a bustling, neighborly, sociable person and had
quickly found a circle of congenial companions, widowed
like herself. And she had kept her eye out for eligible
sons for Nellie, but to no avail. Since Nellie was now the
breadwinner and went her own way without inter-
ference, the relationship between mother and daughter

had changed. But occasionally the mother was moved to protest. "It just isn't natural," she insisted, "not having friends your own age."

"I have friends."

"Who? That Mrs. Hetty Green? She's older than I am and most peculiar."

"Well, she fascinates me. I interviewed her and she took a liking to me. Her mind—it's just like a steel trap. And she has beaten Wall Street at its own game, quite a thing for a woman. I understand she's the wealthiest woman in the whole country."

"And she flatters you that you have a great head for business, too. But I still say you should be thinking of some young man instead, and of getting married."

Nellie brushed this aside. "There's plenty of time for that. I'll get around to it one of these days." How could she explain how completely absorbing her job was? How it took up all her mind, her emotions, her waking and sleeping thoughts, so that there just wasn't time for anything else? True, there were times when other emotions intruded themselves, but these always vanished with the challenge of a new assignment.

Nevertheless, she was disturbed, both by her mother and Mrs. Lockwood. It might even have led to a change in her, except that something of great importance occurred.

Nellie received a royal summons.

# 8

Of the *World* staff, only a handful had ever visited the yacht on which Joseph Pulitzer lived. Moored sometimes in the New York harbor, sometimes farther north on the coast, this yacht was both the home and the office of the publisher. From here he issued his orders for the running of both the *World* and the St. Louis *Post-Dispatch*.

It was not a mere peculiarity that dictated this way of life for Pulitzer. He must have quiet. His early years in America had been ones of terrible poverty and deprivation. He had gone through the Civil War when barely out of his teens. His health was shattered. Since the slightest noise was excruciatingly painful, rooms had to be soundproofed. They must also be darkened because light was unbearable for his eyes. On the yacht he could be close to the city yet away from the uproar and bustle.

In spite of his handicaps he was still in control of his newspapers. His mind was just as tough, just as brilliant, just as incisive as it had ever been. But those he wanted to see must come to him.

Nellie was rowed out from the pier. As she was put on board, she heard the laughter of a child and the soft murmur of a woman answering. It seemed out of place.

But as she walked the length of the deck, she could catch a glimpse of luxurious, well-ordered saloon rooms that were surprisingly homelike.

In his twilight-darkened room, the great publisher rose to meet her.

"Come in, Nellie. Take off your coat—here, this is a comfortable chair." He sat down at his own desk. His long, thin fingers tugged gently at his silky, curling beard. Behind their glasses, his eyes studied her.

"You must have wondered why I seemed to take so little personal interest in your work on the paper. But I have. I have watched your work very closely." He smiled at her. "There have been very few assignments you have taken that I did not know about before you went out on them. Tell me, Nellie, what does it feel like now—to be the first newspaperwoman in the United States? With a job you know you have earned? A little different than that day you fought for three hours to get in and see us, is it not?"

She answered him with a self-assured smile. "Very different. I can hardly remember that day or believe that I am that girl. So much has happened. . . ."

She talked on—of her stories, of incidents, of the paper itself.

While she talked his ears were hearing more than her words, his eyes seeing more than just her presence. He heard the new note, the poised, self-confidence of her, and he found himself ruefully missing the little Nellie he had listened to behind her back that first day in his office. She would never know how deeply she had stirred him then, by her very insecurity, by the stammering, intense, naïve quality of her. It had seemed to him then that she was hammering on his door with her very fists, just as he had had to hammer on closed doors when he was her age. It was unfair of him, he knew, to regret that she was no longer so young or so anxious. Neither was he. They had both come up the hard way. They had arrived—he in his field, she in hers. And if some sensitive, touching quality in her had been lost, he had to remember that she had had to fight not only for her profession but for her sex.

He became conscious that she had finished speaking and was looking at him, puzzled, waiting for him to speak. His tone quickly became businesslike. "You have been doing very well. Two things I read first every Sunday—my editorials and your stories. Now Jules tells me you have another idea. It was not one he wished to decide alone. It was too big; he must have my decision."

"My trip around the world!" Nellie flashed into eager excitement. It could only be that. She had thought Chambers, the city editor, had definitely turned it down.

"What is it you wish to do?" Pulitzer was asking. He had lowered his own voice, as if in gentle hint to her.

She almost whispered, but the intensity came through. "I want to travel completely around the world—by myself. I want to beat Jules Verne's record. It's never been done and people say it can't be done. Since Verne wrote his book *Around the World in Eighty Days*, everyone is talking and wondering if it really would ever be possible to travel as fast as that. His hero Phileas Fogg did it in eighty days—I want to make it in less—with no special help, no chartered ships or holding trains for me! I know the difficulties, Mr. Pulitzer, but I think they are much exaggerated. I got around in Mexico when other people said they couldn't!"

In 1889 travel was just beginning to emerge from the horse-and-buggy days. Trains there were, but they were still somewhat of a marvel; they still did not reach to the smaller, outlying towns. The big cities of Europe and America had fine railroads; steamships came into their harbors. But the stagecoach was still the way for the great majority of people. Parts of the world were still so backward they did not even have stagecoaches; nor were they used to the idea of a woman traveling alone.

This was what bothered Pulitzer.

"It would be possible," he agreed. "But for a young woman! You will be in countries where women are not even seen on the streets unless veiled and escorted. But"—raising his hand to check her pleadings—"you don't have to argue with me. I have already decided you should go. At first I didn't think so. Eighty days! It's incredible."

She was so excited she could hardly speak. "I know. I know. My uncle Thomas Kennedy made a trip around the world and it took him three years and made him an invalid for life." Nellie paused to control both her voice and her excitement. "I'm not afraid for myself. I learned in Mexico that everyone thinks American women are a little crazy, anyway. They make special allowances for that."

"Ah!" he cried softly, deeply, like a lover speaking the name of his beloved— "America! That is why I am interested in this idea. It will be a great newspaper story, the greatest of our age perhaps. But more than that: it would show the world what Americans and America can do. There is something so impudent about it. The world says it cannot be done; the world is satisfied that the old order never changes. Every country stays put in its own little puddle, and we send a girl—a tiny little girl!—to do something that none of their biggest men have done, to break down boundaries and barriers and time itself."

He went on talking about America in a rambling, almost unconnected way.

"It is a great country. It has a great thing—democracy. I was born a Jew in Hungary. My mother was German. I came here for one thing: democracy and progress. To me they mean the same thing. I came to escape being a soldier for a king. And what do I do?" He smiled, and she wondered to herself how she could ever have thought him ugly. There was nobility in the strong, bony face. "The minute I land here I enlisted in the Union Army. Because I knew we were fighting against slavery and slavery holds back progress not only for the black man, but for the white man as well."

She was curious. "But you are always criticizing people, saying the *World* fights the railroads and the government. . . ."

"It is not so! We fight the grabbers. I am afraid for this country, too, Nellie. We grow so fast, we are too rich, too powerful. We open up a continent and find gold and iron and silver and rich lands—and it is all going to the grabbers. They spoil the land, they spoil the government, they spoil this word 'democracy.'" His voice rose as if in pain. Then it steadied. "But we have democracy to fight for, and that is what we can show the rest of the world."

He smiled apologetically. "You must not be upset. I am a newspaperman and that makes me a politician.

[ 141 ]

Politics is my passion—not politics in the general, selfish sense, but politics in the sense of liberty and freedom and ideals of justice. A newspaper can fight for these things. It has a great responsibility. When a newspaper takes the side of the rich against the poor—then is the time to be afraid."

"The *World* never will!" She said hotly.

"I hope you are right," he said, making a turn around the room, pulling a velvet curtain closer across one of the portholes. "Now—for your trip. This is not an excursion into a city street. This is news that will be international. We will arrange for you to send stories daily, and have special courier service to get them onto ships. Small pilot ships will meet the big ones and get your messages off quickly. You must use cables—forget expense. We will have researchers prepare material for you on the countries you are to visit. Huge maps will be printed so that our readers can cut them out of the paper, hang them on their walls and follow your journey step by step." This was Pulitzer the newspaperman, his creative imagination growing. "We will build this day by day and if you beat the record—Nellie, you will be a part of history!"

She was dizzy. What had been a crazy idea, as Chambers had called it, had now become a sober fact. She was going around the world!

Pulitzer picked up her coat and held it for her. The interview was over. He put a hand on her shoulder and shook it a little, affectionately. "You will be our unofficial ambassador to the Old World. But for now, you must not say anything to anyone. Let a word of this get out and all kinds of people will start to race you—try to get there first. As soon as all the details are taken care of, you will hear from us."

A door opened. A woman was silhouetted in the opening. The room was too dark, the light behind her too strong, for Nellie to see her face.

"Joseph, it is getting late. You mustn't overtire yourself or your visitor. It is Miss Bly, isn't it? Nellie Bly? I have wanted to meet you." The voice was low and charming.

"My wife, Nellie. This is Mrs. Pulitzer." He spoke in a teasing way then. "I fought in the Civil War, on the side of the North. And I won a prize. Just like the warriors of old, I carry off a bride from the enemy. My wife is a cousin of Jefferson Davis," he explained.

"That old joke! Now, Joseph, you rest. I'll walk with Miss Bly to the gangway."

As Nellie climbed down into the small boat to take her ashore, she looked back at the woman waving from above. The lights framed Kate Pulitzer's face. Why, she's beautiful! Nellie thought. She felt a pang for a moment. What would it be like to be safely married like this woman—married and beloved of a man like Joseph Pulitzer, the mother of his children?

Then she put the thought away, quickly. It was not Kate Pulitzer, or any other woman, who was to have a trip around the world, to be the first to make such a great adventure. It was she, Nellie Bly. She hugged herself in rapturous anticipation.

But the next few days were sheer torture: waiting, waiting, wondering, hoping, expecting—telling herself each day that surely Pulitzer would announce definite plans. Finally she became stern with herself. She would *not* think about it. She would forget it, go about her busi-

[ 143 ]

ness, not count on it. Nellie began a series of articles on swindlers who claimed to teach scarfmaking and glove-making to women who wanted a trade.

She was returning one day to the *World* Building when she saw a copy boy on the steps making frantic motions for her to hurry.

"I've been looking everywhere for you, Miss Bly!" he panted. "No one knew—Mr. Chamber's been yellin' his head off for the last two hours!"

Nellie flew up the stairs. If this was it!—then this was the moment she had been building up to; everything she had ever done was in preparation for this moment!

It was.

"I'm sorry to do this to you, Nellie," Jules Chambers said apologetically, urgency and excitement in his voice. "It isn't giving you any time at all to get ready. Can you possibly leave for your trip in forty-eight hours?"

"Forty-eight *hours*? I have to plan an itinerary, figure out the route. . . ."

"That's already been done. And the *Augusta Victoria* leaves for England day after tomorrow; if we can book passage on it, the schedule is already being worked out for connections with railroads and ships and coaches. Can you do it?"

She thought swiftly. "I can! But what about passports, visas, letters to banks for credits, travel money. . . ."

"We'll take care of that, too. What I'm worried about is you—your clothes and such."

She was appalled. What about clothes—and baggage? And if she took trunks and baggage then how could she manage them? She knew from experience that a little thing like getting trunks cleared through ship quarantine or through customs could delay a traveler sometimes for hours. It could lose her the whole race.

Still worrying about it, Nellie went to Ghormley's.

The fashionable dress salon was delighted. For a trip of this kind the customer would need suits, coats, dresses for warm weather, for cold weather, evening dresses, morning dresses, raincoats, dressing gowns, cloaks, tea gowns. Sketches were produced. It would be possible, if they hurried, to get them all ready in three weeks.

"That just isn't possible," she declared. "I must have something in forty-eight hours. And I want just one coat, an ulster and two dresses—and that's all." To the chorus of indignant protests, she was deaf. She picked up one sketch. "Now, this one—if you eliminate the big bustle, make the lines straighter, then I could wear this anywhere. And just one other dress that can be crushed into a suitcase and not wrinkle too much—a light silk pongee, perhaps."

"Just two dresses?" Madam Ghormley was scandalized.

"And a coat."

This was no problem. By the greatest of luck, there was a coat already made in the salon, ordered for a customer who had changed her mind. It was a good camel's hair, checked, and it fitted. Furthermore, there was a cap to match. The cap, especially, pleased Nellie since it was on the order of a jockey cap, tight fitting, with a small brimmed visor over her eyes.

"But only *two* dresses!" the seamstress wailed. "And you want them by. . . ."

"By tonight. No later. I'll be too busy to do anything about them tomorrow."

Ghormley's was galvanized into action. It was not just

the money, it was the advertising. A trip around the world was a fantastic idea for which there would be much publicity, and if the *World* were just to mention where she had her dresses made . . .? Nellie assured them this would be done, and the fitting was ordered promptly.

Back at the *World*, Nellie plunged again into a whirlwind of activities. Plans were made and changed and remade again, hour after hour; discussions, debates and arguments raged. The travel bureau of the paper was called upon to help plan her route. Cables were dispatched to Southampton, to London, to Paris, to Brindisi in Italy, to Cairo and to Peking and Yokohama, as the route began to take shape and to assume proportions of what train to catch, what ships, what hotels. Some of this could be managed while Nellie was crossing the Atlantic but at least a few connections had to be made immediately.

Cables were sent, too, to American consuls in the bigger cities of Europe. Special arrangements with government offices cut red tape to get the necessary passport for her.

It was decided she should cable her most important stories and send the others by fast mail trains and courier service. There might be days in which no stories would arrive on time, so two staff men were assigned to write fill-in stories of the countries she would be visiting.

Nellie was beset by plans, schemes, ideas—most of which she regretfully had to abandon. A visit to Charles Dickens in London, an audience with English royalty, a conference with the leading women suffragists of Europe, a look-in at the Sultan of Morocco—these would have made exciting stories but she would have no time for them.

Back at Ghormley's at three o'clock for another fitting. The traveling dress was of blue broadcloth and a becoming shade of blue it was; the summer dress was yellow muslin. Then the bank to draw out two hundred pounds in English gold and Bank of England notes, half that much more in American paper money and gold. She wrote hasty notes to her family and friends, tidied up some loose ends on her newspaper correspondence, packed two "ghillie" caps—similar to the jockey kind Ghormley's was altering for her—three veils, some slippers, a dressing gown, a jacket, several changes of flannel underwear, handkerchiefs, cold cream, toilet articles, needles, thread—and a supply of paper and pencils.

At ten that evening both dresses were finished. She was packed and ready to leave.

On the morning of November 14, 1889, a small group of fifteen people gathered at the New Jersey pier to see her off on the steamer *Augusta Victoria*. Her mother said tearful good-byes. A few people cheered. An artist sketched her as she went up the gangplank, but before that an important ceremony had taken place. Solemnly, Nellie and Chambers and an official of the steamship company adjusted and compared their watches. She left American soil at exactly three seconds after nine-forty in the morning. No matter where she was she would keep that watch set to American time. The days and hours and minutes, the winning or the losing of her race with time, would be calculated in American hours.

[ 147 ]

## 9

She was at sea when the story broke into headlines in the *World*:

## A CONTINUOUS TRIP WHICH WILL GIRDLE THE SPINNING GLOBE

## NELLIE BLY TO MAKE AN UNEQUALED RAPID-TRANSIT RECORD

## NOW 30,000 MILES IN A RUSH

## CAN JULES VERNE'S GREAT DREAM BE REDUCED TO ACTUAL FACT?

The *World* today undertakes the task of turning a dream into reality. . . . Nellie Bly, so well known to millions who have read of her doings, as told by her captivating pen, will set out as a female Phileas Fogg and if nothing prevents . . . will report back . . . in just 75 days.

The crossing of the Atlantic was a ghastly one, storm tossed and terrifying. Passengers were too ill to get out of their staterooms, except for the hardy few. Nellie wasn't ill but the effort of trying to keep her feet on a deck that slid and pitched and tossed her around like a tennis ball was too much. She was glad when the ship docked at Southampton.

It was two-thirty in the morning and a carriage was waiting. Her train ticket for London was held for her at the station. The connections planned in New York were clicking along smoothly. At her London hotel were further instructions brought along by the London correspondent for the *World*.

"You are to sail tomorrow for Italy," he told her.

But she wasn't listening. Among the shower of letters and telegrams of encouragement and praise and commendation was one from Jules Verne, inviting her to visit him in France.

"I can't miss that opportunity!" she explained to her London co-worker. "It would make too good a story. We'll just have to arrange the trip a little differently."

He was shocked. "It can't be done! One side trip like that and you'll lose the race—you'll never make it in seventy-five days."

Her mind was made up, however. Hunting frantically, the two of them found a packet boat leaving England immediately; they read train schedules and found one that would leave Calais, France, in time for her to meet the boat at Brindisi. It would mean split-second timing, otherwise all the tour arrangements for transportation would be nullified and the trip itself a failure. It would mean sitting up in boats and trains without sleep for two nights. To Nellie it was well worth it. Jules Verne had written the book, famous throughout the world, which had become the springboard for her whole idea; his hero Phileas Fogg was her opponent in this race.

Though it was early when she left London, she had her first taste of the excitement which her trip was spreading throughout the world. People lined up in front of her hotel to cheer her, and dockworkers crowded around to see her off.

The trip to Amiens, France, where Verne lived was something Nellie never liked to recall afterward. She spent sleepless nights, one of them aboard a rickety old boat crossing the Channel, the other on a jolting ride by train to Amiens. She was exhausted when she arrived.

The sight of Jules Verne and Mrs. Verne at the railroad station to meet her brought tears to her eyes. She had not expected such kindness. It was a proud and happy moment and her tiredness left her magically. They went on treating her with the same tender thoughtfulness—this "child" who was so brave, so courageous, so little. They drove her to their beautiful, luxurious home where a fire was burning in the velvet-hung sitting room, and a tea tray sat on the low table in front of the fire.

When Nellie explained that she must leave immediately to catch her train to Calais, they were horrified. She had had no sleep, no rest!—at least, she must sit awhile and talk to them. This is what she wanted. She was a reporter; she wanted to squeeze every possible moment out of this visit—to talk and to listen.

They talked of America, of France, of Jules Verne's books and, of course, of her trip. Kindly Jules Verne warned her: "I do not think you can make it, but you must not be downhearted by that. You will have made the try. And someday it will be done." Mrs. Verne teased her a little about perhaps catching a husband on the trip. After all, she was a romantic figure, this little Nellie Bly—was there no romance in her life?

None, she answered firmly. "I'm just too busy to think about romance, not with trains to catch and boats to think of."

This reminded them that time was running out. Verne took her to his study first. It was impressive to Nellie because of the monklike, severe quality of it. It was a room to work in, in sharp contrast to the luxury of the rest of the house. Here he had written *Around the World in Eighty Days* and *Twenty Thousand Leagues Under the Sea* and many others. Here he lived in a world of his own fertile, creative, farseeing imagination, writing of things that were prophetic of scientific discoveries of the future.

She raced for the station, barely making her train. That night she found she must sleep in the same compartment with twenty-two other passengers. In other circumstances she might have been too modest; but utter exhaustion made her indifferent. All she cared about were a pillow and a mattress and sleep.

At Brindisi the train was two hours late.

This was disaster. Connections between it and the steamer had had to be figured in minutes. Now she was *two hours* late. And it had been her own headstrong, reckless decision to see Verne that had brought her to this failure. How could she go back and face Pulitzer? Remembering that little crowd of cheering workers at the dock in England, she felt physically sick with frustration and disappointment.

Her hired carriage finally came in sight of the Brindisi docks. She stared for a moment with unbelieving eyes, then, to the amazement and the scandal of the carriage driver and the porters, the American girl gave a wild whoop of joy, threw a handful of coins into the box of the driver, lifted up her skirts with one hand, her satchels with the other and ran, pell-mell, down to the docks. The *Augusta Victoria* was still in port! It had purposely waited to make connections with the mail train.

Now at last on board, she felt that she was finally off on her journey into the unknown.

She made friends. Descriptions of them went into her stories. She made an enemy. And Americans reading about the purser of the ship, who was so outraged at the idea of this woman traveling alone that he had given her a small, crowded cabin instead of the one she was entitled to, forced her to wait for the second serving—when there was little food left!—and in general treated her with scorn—when Americans read this in the *World* stories they would all have enjoyed horsewhipping that purser.

All over America, people were following her journey with a tremendous interest that grew and grew. The *World* was not exaggerating when it said "The whole civilized world is watching Nellie Bly." Even though other New York newspapers laughed at the idea that she could actually make it in less than eighty days, nevertheless they could not ignore her. Their readers, too, demanded to know every day just where Nellie was—how far along she had traveled—what was happening to her.

The Pittsburgh *Dispatch* was even prouder than the *World*. They had given Nellie her start and they publicly called attention to this. Other Pittsburgh papers—the same ones that had protested her stories before—now leaped onto the band wagon to hail her as their own beloved favorite daughter. Throughout the country, wherever the *World* could be bought, it was handed from person to person; circulation went up and up. Where it couldn't be bought local newspapers copied their stories for their readers. Chicago, Baltimore, Auburn, Maine, Washington—everywhere people read about Nellie Bly.

And their letters poured into the *World*.

"Was Nellie Bly really a woman?" The *World* staff answered this inquiry until they were sick of it. "What does she look like?" "A very pretty brunette," they answered. "Send us her picture—tell us more about her." The *World* found they had become an answering service, a matrimonial bureau (as proposals to Nellie came pouring in), the recipient of all kinds of advice and warnings and friendly comments. People wanted to marry Nellie, adopt her, honor her—or scold her.

The letters became an avalanche.

Songs were written about her. Verses appeared. An enterprising manufacturer made and sold a "Nellie Bly wrapper" for ladies in their undress morning moments.

The *World* began a Nellie Bly game, one that could be played with markers for her progress and chances on what exact minute she would arrive at her various destinations. Other games appeared. Gamblers became interested and bets were laid—heavy ones—as to the odds on whether she would make it and on the exact time of her arrival home.

Seldom in history had the excitement, the interest, the feverish curiosity of a whole nation been so aroused and pinned on the adventures of one small individual.

Her cables arrived regularly. In between times the *World* ran stories of the countries her boat was passing, of storms that other ships had encountered in that area, of customs aboard ship—nothing seemed too trivial or too small to be hungrily read by Nellie's fans.

On board the *Augusta Victoria,* Nellie was having her troubles breaking down the traditional British reserve. But occasionally it broke too far. She was proposed to twice.

She had noticed one particular gentleman with great astonishment. Not a day passed, in fact hardly an afternoon, when he did not have a complete change of wardrobe. The gossip had spread that he had nineteen trunks of clothing in his stateroom! Now he sought her out. He asked her, frankly and abruptly, to marry him and just as frankly told her why:

"I always killed the desire to love and marry because I never expected to find a woman who could travel without innumerable trunks and bundles." Nellie's one gripsack and one ghillie had excited as much comment among the passengers as had this elegant dandy's nineteen trunks.

She asked him, point-blank, how many trunks he had. He confirmed the rumor. Trying hard to keep from laughing in his face, Nellie solemnly thanked him for his offer, said that she realized the honor was due to her one gripsack and not to her other charms, then fled to her stateroom to laugh until she cried.

The other proposal was an equally practical one. A handsome young Englishman had been following her about for days, trying in vain to get her alone. Finally one romantic, moonlit evening he succeeded. He walked with her to a secluded spot and there unburdened his heart. Because he was the second son in his family, any money and any property would naturally go to the oldest. It was up to him to scratch for himself—and in his eyes, the best way to go about it would be to find a wife who would settle a thousand pounds a year on him. The steward on the ship had told him Nellie was a wealthy and eccentric heiress—it must be true because only the most wealthy could care so little about conventions that she could be content with but two dresses in her wardrobe!

He loved her, of course—madly.

Nellie asked him if he would love her just as much if he were to find out that she was not a wealthy heiress, but a poor girl being sent around the world by a charity society for her health?

This time it was the suitor who fled.

And back home Americans laughed and jeered at these fortune hunters along with their Nellie. She would show them! And they shared her pleasure as she finally came to know the rest of the people on board and rapidly became a popular figure with them.

The voyage through the Mediterranean, through the Suez Canal, through the Red Sea—was delayed by weather conditions. December 14th found her in Colombo, Ceylon, a little behind schedule. She worried, but since there was nothing to be done about it, she scampered over the island enjoying herself, filling her cables with the odd, the picturesque, the grand and the trivial. Her stories had the knack of conveying to the reader all the breathless astonishment and delight she herself found in each new discovery—whether it was the magnificence of the harbor and the mountains behind it or the habits of the English there who lived lives of indolent luxury, the women in smart frocks reading novels, the men in their white tropicals smoking cigars and lounging on hotel verandas. What a contrast they made to the natives who wore so little and worked so hard!

She rode a bicycle on the island. She had one unusual experience: a midnight drive during which she was pulled by bullocks, those great oxen of the East. She also had her first jinrikisha trip. She talked to merchants, to priests—and the only time she regretted her lack of a wardrobe was when she had to refuse an invitation to a dinner because her own muslin dress was unsuitable. On the whole, the two dresses were holding up well, though it meant constant cleaning and pressing and watchfulness if they were to clothe her decently for the whole trip.

America marveled. Such words as these—temple priests and jinrikishas—had come out of the pages of dusty encyclopedias and were now part of their own experience—through her eyes.

From Colombo she went to Canton, China. Here, while she sent cables telling of everything she saw, there was one story she did not write. It had to do with one of the worst moments of her life.

The first person to see her in Singapore was a consular official. With him was a newspaperman.

They greeted her warmly. "We've been waiting a good many anxious days for this, Miss Bly! Newspapers from home have been driving us crazy with questions: 'Has she arrived yet? Where is she? How is she?' It does us good to see you looking so well. We were afraid you'd be feeling very unhappy."

"Unhappy? Why, for goodness sakes!"

"Because of that other woman—that other reporter."

"*What* other reporter! I don't know what you are talking about."

The two men looked at each other, startled and alarmed, then back to Nellie.

"You mean you don't know that a Miss Elizabeth Bisland started out to beat you, going the other way? And that she is way ahead of you? She passed through here quite a while ago."

Nellie stared at them in complete unbelief and horror. Her mind was in chaos, her heart in pieces. She was going to be beaten!—and by another woman, a woman who had leaped onto her idea and was now going to steal the race, the glory and the prize from underneath her very hands.

Somehow she managed not to show all she felt. She even tried to smile. "How do you know she is ahead?"

"All the reports say that. I'm terribly sorry, Miss Bly. I didn't realize you knew nothing of this. It must come as an awful shock to you."

What was she going to do about it? What *could* she do but go on as best she could, make a decent showing and pretend to be a good sport about it? But she had heard nothing of this from the *World.* Perhaps it wasn't true. Perhaps there was no Miss Bisland. No, a newspaperman and a consul would not repeat a rumor out of thin air. It must be that the *World* had kept the news from her to save her feelings and to make sure she would continue, anyway. After all, it was still her own idea and even if she couldn't win, she could share a little in the credit.

Singapore had plenty of material for her stories. Just as at home, Nellie went everywhere—into slums, into office buildings, into spacious residential areas, into hospitals and churches and dock wharves and factories. She even bought a monkey. Then, en route to Canton, China, the ship ran into a terrific storm. Badly shaken as she was, when they landed she went off sight-seeing immediately. It seemed to her that suffering of that kind was as nothing compared to the inward suffering of knowing that everything she now did was empty, a form to go through, because she owed at least that much to the *World*.

Sometimes she felt a surge of real hope. She could still win. Elizabeth Bisland might run into transportation or weather difficulties—anything might happen. Then her hopes would spin back down to earth. There was nothing she could do to hurry her own fate, and if the other woman was already ahead, the chances of her winning were assured.

At Yokohama, she was exactly fifty days from her starting time. There were only twenty-seven days left— to catch a ship, to cross an ocean and then a continent. In those days, when ocean travel was figured in weeks, not days, this left her no margin for safety. In spite of that, her spirits were raised by the reception she received in Japan. It was her second hint of the international interest in her. The Jules Verne interview had been translated into Japanese and printed in their papers; the correspondent there for the World, a Japanese, had fed the national press story after story on Nellie Bly. She was met by Japanese officials, escorted proudly around the city by important men of affairs and her arrival was heralded by the blowing of steamship whistles in the harbor. As she was driven through the streets, the train of carriages and carts following her became an impromptu parade; when she stopped, people came pressing forward to touch her strange American dress, to stare at the spectacle of this amazing girl traveler, and to wish her well in the strange foreign tongue, the words of which she couldn't understand but the meaning of which was clear.

On January 7th, the steamship *Oceanic* sailed out of the harbor for home. As Nellie arrived at the dock, the band struck up "Hail, Columbia," and she wanted to cry out loud with the surging pride in those dear, familiar strains and with the homesickness they brought her. Then the band switched to "The Girl I Left Behind Me." She noticed a huge sign printed on the side of the ship—"For Nellie Bly—We'll win or die!" She wasn't alone! It wasn't only she who was running this race; this whole ship and its officers and passengers were pulling for her, hoping and praying for her.

It was a moment of high emotion. As the ship sailed slowly out, the haunting music of "Home, Sweet Home" brought new tears to her eyes. Perhaps she had lost to this other woman, but it had still been worth it.

From the first day out the ship was in trouble. And on the third day the storms hit. The small ocean liner was tossed about by the high, heavy waves, the pouring rain, the winds that screamed along the decks and tore the ship from its course, sending it plunging and rolling through day after day of dark horror.

[ 159 ]

The passengers were terrified. Even the crew was frightened.

Word was sent along to the captain and through him relayed to Nellie. It was her fault, this storm, because she had brought a monkey on board and monkeys were traditionally bad omens for ships. She would have to get rid of it. It was a jinx.

Nellie refused. Luckily for her, the captain was not superstitious. He also had some understanding of what the monkey meant to her: tangible proof for the people back home of the exotic East she had visited. She was fond of it; it had figured in one of the best stories she had cabled back, and she would fight to keep it. He gave in, cautioning her only to keep it hidden.

The voyage went on. The storms lightened a little, but just the same it was two weeks before the *Oceanic* saw land—the harbor of San Francisco.

Nellie looked at it with mixed emotions. Excitement, longing, happiness, fear and reluctance—they warred inside of her, and overriding all else a great, overwhelming longing for that bit of land, for that city she could glimpse and for all the land, all the cities, of this her own, wonderful country.

But even as she could feel the land almost underneath her foot, a new hazard arose. A rumor of smallpox on board threatened to quarantine all passengers and prevent them from landing. This was one delay she would not tolerate. Sweeping all objections away, overriding all arguments, she demanded to be put ashore. And she was—in a small tug that landed her, her monkey and her baggage onto the San Francisco dock, alone of all the *Oceanic* passengers.

[ 160 ]

Quickly a doctor examined her. She was passed. Gathering up her luggage she looked around his small office for the door. But the doctor stopped her.

"Just one moment." He took off his gown. "Now! Miss Bly, will you permit me. . . ?" He gave her his arm and motioned to an attendant to pick up her luggage. "This way, please."

They walked out to the waiting room.

And then came the uproar, confusion, shouts, crowds. Nellie stood, unbelieving. The wharf was thronged, jammed with so many people that nothing could be seen but the masses of thousands of human bodies, nothing could be heard above the roar of thousands of voices screaming "Nellie! Nellie Bly! Hurrah for Nellie!" In vain did a top-hatted delegation of the San Francisco mayor, the entire San Francisco Press Club and other dignitaries try to carry her off. The flowers they gave her were almost torn from her hands—their words were lost in the tumult of the crowds. Bands played, people sang: "My Nellie's Blue Eyes" and the Stephen Foster song for which she was named.

If the whole of America had been waiting for her, San Francisco was not to be outdone. As the carriage drove her to the railroad station, it seemed to her that everyone in the city was in the streets filling every curb to see her go by. The shouts were a roar that swelled with each moment.

They cried for a speech and she tried to speak:

"There's no place like home," she told them through happy tears. "For sixty-eight days I've been dashing around the world and am once again back in America. The saddest sounds were the farewells from the Hoboken pier—the sweetest sounds the words of welcome and applause in San Francisco."

It is doubtful if many heard. But they were satisfied to see her and to claim her as their own, their Nellie Bly. Ahead of her carriage marched a strong band of women suffragists with their banners flying. Behind her were carriages and bands and marchers that made a parade blocks long. Beside her in the open brougham rode the West Coast correspondent for the *World*. In the midst of all the excitement Nellie had an opportunity to ask him:

"What about this Elizabeth Bisland? Has she really beat me?"

He gave her a horrified look. "Where did you ever hear such a thing! Wait a minute—yes, there was a woman who started out—right after you left. She wasn't a newspaper woman; she worked for a magazine. But she had to give up and come back."

Now Nellie's cup was full and running over. The relief was so great, the noise around her so deafening, so uproarious, that she started to shake. She wanted to laugh and cry, all at the same time. This welcome home really *was* for her—she had earned it and it was *all* hers.

Ranchers, farmers, sheepherders and cowboys rode hundreds of miles just to stand at a way station and see her train go by. City railroad depots were mobbed. The train itself carried great pennants with her name on them. She was impatient for that train to go on, make good time, but there many unscheduled stops along the tracks, where they found seas of people drawn from every village, every town, every farm within a hundred-mile radius. Nellie spoke, shook hands and was cheered and

[ 162 ]

loved and applauded. And she had been so right to protect the monkey against the superstitions of the *Oceanic's* crew; everyone, everywhere, wanted to see that monkey curled on her shoulder.

In Kansas suffragists pleaded with her to come back and run for governor of the state.

In Chicago she was carried off the train on the shoulders of members of the Press Club.

But when her train steamed into Jersey City, where she was to debark for the final estimate of the days and minutes of her journey, then the celebration really began to let off steam. She touched the soil of New Jersey exactly seventy-two days, six hours and ten minutes from the time she had left that soil at Hoboken.

And at that moment, at 3:15 P.M. on January 26th, the race was won. Not only had she equaled the record of Jules Verne's hero; she had bettered it. She had gone around the world in less time than anyone else ever had; she, a woman, had gone alone and unescorted, and had proved that the world was no longer a place divided—in travel at least. Three stop watches, her own included, registered the fact.

All the whistles in Jersey City let off one tremendous blast at the news. The crowds, held back by the police until that moment, broke through the restraining cordon and swept down upon her and the small groups of *World* staff members with her. She was seized, held high above the crowd at times, allowed to walk a few steps and then seized again. Men and women screamed and yelled; in a great surge of honest sentiment there were many who cried. Her littleness, her very femininity, made her victory seem all the more tremendous.

If the mayor of Jersey City could not be heard, at least his speech was read in the papers that day:

The American girl can no longer be misunderstood! She will be recognized as determined, independent, able to take care of herself wherever she may go. You have added another spark to the great beacon light of American liberty. People the world over have been taught that they are not as far apart as they imagined. You have set the whole world to thinking about it and so have brought mankind closer together. Welcome home—Nellie Bly!

New York's reception was even greater. They had had time—and the direction of the *World*—in which to organize her homecoming. From the Bowery to the farthest uptown reaches, from the East River to the Hudson, the streets were packed with people moving to catch a glimpse of her as the parade moved from the railroad station to the office of the *World* on Park Row. City officials, state officials, the Governor, all were on hand to welcome her.

But for Nellie, the greatest moment of all was her first sight of the *World* Building with its golden dome—and the sight of Joseph Pulitzer himself on hand, inside where it was quieter, to greet her.

"Well done, little Nellie," he said, softly. "You have won. I knew you would." He showed her the headline in the paper of that morning:

### FATHER TIME OUTDONE!

He was especially proud of the report of one of the London papers, which said:

It is an idea none but an American newspaper could have conceived, and none but an American girl could successfully have carried out.

She was home again, but it was not the same. She was now an international figure, a national heroine, a permanent part of history.

# 10

The uproar over her trip, and the aftermath of it, left Nellie completely bewildered. She lost her bearings. There was a feeling of unreality about everything, as if she had become a different person. For a while New York seemed a different place; because there were no new assignments, no writing for her, she did not even have the comfort of the old, familiar routine.

She was taken up by a new group of people: socialites, the wealthy—eager for any new attraction—and the hangers-on, people who liked to be seen with celebrities. Her former companions, the newspapermen, no longer felt that as a woman she had invaded their territory. Her exploits had gone beyond that. But they were apt either to put her on a pedestal as "the greatest newspaper feature of the age" or to consider her as having deserted *them* for her new friends. James Metcalfe of the *Life* magazine of that day was the only one who dared poke fun at her. He wrote a satire of her trip around the world and called it "Sadie McGinty and her trip around Manhattan Island." Nellie was furious. The time had long passed when she would poke fun at herself or permit anyone else to.

She was the darling of society, the toast of the town. She was feted, wined, dined and courted by influential people. When Nellie walked into a drawing room or dining room and her name was announced, there would be the hush of conversation, then the crowding around, the eagerness of people to say they had talked to her or touched her or looked at her. Even though her independent mind knew that this was a passing thing and that she was being put on exhibition much as these wealthy ones would present their guests with a new dish for their appetites or a new entertainment, nevertheless Nellie could not escape liking the adulation, the luxury, the beauty and the richness of these homes where she was now welcome.

It was at an evening musicale that she met Robert Seamon.

The musicians had performed; soon, she knew, she would be asked to speak on her trip. Nellie was relaxing on a sofa near the fireplace, grateful for the cheerful blaze of the fire, conscious of the curious glances being sent her way, cordial to the guests as they came up, one by one, to speak to her and to congratulate her.

At first Seamon's was just one among a sea of faces, which she didn't even try to remember. But when he returned the second and the third time, bringing her a glass of punch, conducting a waiter with a tray of canapés, thoughtfully adjusting the screen so that the fire would not scorch her face, then she was forced to notice him. It was a novelty for her to be so well taken care of.

"It's a pleasure for me," he said, acknowledging her thanks. Robert Seamon was a much older man, courtly, kind and dignified. "I have followed your writing in the *World* for years," he continued. "I admire your courage in making your race over the globe—but I must admit that I admire much more the picture you make in that blue satin gown. You are lovely, my dear."

Nellie was startled. How seldom in her life had a man noticed how she looked! She saw the open and honest admiration in his eyes and was warmed by it.

Seamon was also very rich and influential. This first meeting led to others. Accompanied by her mother as chaperone, she became a frequent guest in his home and each time she went she was more charmed by the beauty his wealth had created, by the culture of his friends, by his library with its thousands of books and, most of all, by Seamon's own genuine delight in her. It was dazzling to be in the company of prominent men and women— merchants, manufacturers, heads of colleges, respected doctors, lawyers—and not to feel that she was there merely on exhibition but rather an equal.

It wasn't long, however, before the *World* claimed her services again. Pulitzer was anxious to capitalize on her reputation. He had no objection to her accepting engagements as a lecturer, quite the contrary. Wherever she spoke she publicized his newspaper. Nor did he mind that she took the time to write a book of her experiences. Her income steadily mounted; she was making from twenty to twenty-five thousand a year. Nellie was now a well-to-do woman and could establish herself and her mother in a large and expensive apartment.

But Pulitzer wanted more stories from her. Now that she was a national figure, he wanted stories of national scope.

She was sent to Saratoga to investigate what went on there during the famous racing season. For many years Saratoga had been the center of the fashionable sporting world; it also attracted crooks and vice of every description. Nellie's stories revealed both sides: the magnificence of the hotels, the handsome carriages, the beautifully dressed women, the rich and idle amusing themselves in this pleasure resort, and on the other hand, the dishonesty of race track officials, the depravity and prostitution that flourished on the outskirts of town. While neither side acknowledged the other, neither would have been there alone.

Next she wrote a series of sketches describing each of the big Tammany leaders. New York city had long been controlled by these corrupt politicians. Dr. Parkhurst had campaigned against them, had even had their leader Boss Tweed thrown into jail, but the system still flourished. They promised the people in their districts everything, but did nothing for them, instead spending their time dipping their greedy hands into the public funds. Even though they knew Nellie intended to expose them, so great was their awe of her as a reporter, and so potent her charm, that they let themselves be interviewed—to their own dismay, afterward.

But Nellie's greatest story of the next few years was to take place outside of New York.

In 1894 the American Railway Union was engaged in a fierce, hard-fought labor dispute with the Pullman Palace Car Company. It had begun in a small way, with only a small number of workers involved, as a boycott against Pullman, but it had soon spread to affect nearly every railroad in the country as the union refused to work on any train carrying a Pullman car.

George Pullman, of Pullman, Illinois, was an absolute monarch. He owned the town and he owned the workers. He was both their employer and their landlord. Even in prosperous times wages there were below standard, and these were depression days. One skilled mechanic worked ten hours a day for twelve days and received a pay check of seven cents! His wages had been nine dollars and seven cents but nine dollars rent for his Pullman-owned house had been deducted in advance. A fireman in the shop received forty dollars a month. Others, after their debts for food at the Pullman-owned store and their rent had been taken out of their pay check, found themselves with forty-five cents for a day's work. Many were not employed at all but they owed so much rent they could not move.

The town was run like a feudal manor. No saloons were allowed in it, nothing that might promote "pleasure or idleness." No trade unions existed. Company spies were everywhere—reporting on what the people said, what the wives complained of. They had enough to report: children could not even go to school, not merely that they couldn't afford schoolbooks, but because they had no shoes or clothes. Many children were kept in bed all day, just for the warmth. There was no coal in the houses and little food.

Finally a committee of the workers went to the Pullman management with their grievances. They were told to get out.

On May 11th, three thousand workers at Pullman left their jobs. Because many held secret membership in the

American Railway Union, they called on that union for help. Eugene V. Debs and the other officials responded; support was voted, but as a boycott, not as a strike. Railroad men would work on any railroad, any train, any yard, as long as they did not handle Pullman cars. They promised that federal mail would not be stopped. Nearly a hundred and twenty-five thousand men joined the boycott.

Reprisal was swift. Pullman hired strikebreakers off the streets, many of whom were hoodlums and gangsters who did not hesitate to use guns against the strikers or to burn Pullman property in order to put the blame on the union. Almost without exception, the newspapers believed the reports that the union members were rioting mobs, burning and destroying private property and inciting to anarchy. It was not until long after the strike that a federal investigating commission reported the true facts of the case in the union's favor.

It proved that Debs had been extremely careful in not permitting any destruction of property by his union members; they would not work Pullman cars but neither would they destroy them.

At the time, however, the nation's newspapers screamed in headlines:

FIRED BY THE MOB
CHICAGO AT THE MERCY OF INCENDIARIES'
TORCH

WILD RIOT IN CHICAGO
HUNDREDS OF FREIGHT CARS BURNED
BY STRIKERS

President Cleveland ordered out federal troops. Martial law was declared. Debs and other union leaders were jailed and the boycott was broken.

It was in this atmosphere that Nellie came to Chicago. She went to see Debs in the McHenry County Jail. She found a man, middle-aged, well-dressed, fastidiously neat —quite the opposite of the wild-mannered anarchist she had been led to expect. She was captivated by his gentleness and his humanity, by his laughter and his jokes, and especially by his fierce anger for the plight of the workers.

"Go to the town of Pullman," he advised her. "The other newspapermen hang around here or around the courts or interview the judges. You go see for yourself why those men could no longer live the way they were, and why the rest of the union supported them."

She went to Pullman. She saw for herself that he had not exaggerated when he told her of the poverty and misery. Nellie's stories for the *World* reflected her outraged indignation that American citizens should be treated like serfs, owned body and soul by one man. She wrote: "He even expects them to vote as he says!"

But she had neither sympathy nor understanding for boycotts, strikes or anything that might be called violent action. Her stories were ones that astounded Pulitzer and the readers of the *World*, since so much had been said against the union that people had come to believe them a collection of bomb-throwing radicals. Now Nellie showed the real conditions that had led to the boycott.

She talked again to Debs, but she had little understanding of what he said. Her humanitarian principles were aroused; she was thoroughly angry; she wanted to tell the world of Pullman and Pullman's town. But she had no understanding of what Debs and the American Railway Union was trying to do. She was more impressed by the man himself, by the fact that he seemed to have so little resentment that he was in jail, and over his worry for his parents. She glimpsed something in him of his fighting, passionate beliefs in the rights of labor, and something of his own personal integrity, both of which had made him an adored leader of hundreds of thousands of people.

But her own ideas were hardening and changing. Like Pulitzer, Nellie believed that democracy worked as well for the poor as for the rich—with first a few needed reforms. This head-on collision between labor and capital frightened her. She saw the need to change the town of Pullman, but she felt that she—with her pen spreading the knowledge of it—could do more than the force of a union.

All her life, Nellie Bly was to keep her burning anger at injustice. But no longer did she enjoy baiting and antagonizing factory owners. Wasn't Robert Seamon a factory owner? Wasn't her friend Hetty Green the richest woman in America and a shrewd speculator in Wall Street? Wasn't she herself now a woman of property? It was no longer possible for her to identify herself with a poor workingwoman, a factory slave or a domestic servant. Nellie was now on the other side of the tracks.

She was nearly thirty years old, in those days almost past the age for marrying. She could no longer say to herself: *"Sometime I'll fall in love—sometime, but not right now."* If it wasn't now it might be never.

Belva Lockwood's words came back to her, haunting

her, with the echo of *". . . you're wrong, Nellie!"* Somewhere, Nellie knew, she had made a mistake. She was a solitary figure with no ties, no bonds, no interest outside of her work. Even in her crusading against poverty and injustice, it had always been first the story, then her anger against evil and only last—and sometimes not at all—any feeling of love or compassion or identity with those whose causes she so ably championed. Even when she campaigned against the ill-treatment of women, she was impatient with those who suffered it.

She had fame and professional reputation. But Belva Lockwood had more——she had a close kinship with the men and women with whom she worked. The girls of Pythagoras Hall had their own solid feeling of belonging, of being united for a purpose. Others had family and husbands, friends and companionship.

In the depths of her despondency, Robert Seamon proposed to her.

His attentions had been doubly welcome to her, both because he was a distinguished, attractive man in himself, and because he wrapped her cold loneliness in a warmth of devotion. He was unusually thoughtful of her, respected her mind and praised her as a sharp businesswoman—which she wasn't!—but most of all, he loved her.

He was much older than she. But if she was not to have a young love, a young romance, at least with Robert Seamon she would have affection, a tender consideration, a gentle, undemanding love.

Their marriage was the signal for a storm of scandalous attacks. She was called every kind of name imaginable, gold digger and fortune hunter being among the kindest.

How could such an attractive, lovely girl marry a man twice her age? It could only be his money—or his position in society! That she might genuinely care for Seamon they refused to believe. That she had a large income of her own, they forgot. And "they" included the people at the *World,* as well as the gossips outside of it.

Bill Nye was sorrowfully convinced that her head had been turned by all the glory heaped on her. He was sure she wanted to become one of New York's "four hundred" —and so another name was heaped onto her: social climber.

It was true that for a while Nellie did become something of a socialite. She gave fashionable parties and was a gracious hostess. She brought to Robert Seamon's home her own reputation to intrigue people, her own dash for creating something different and unusual and exciting. People flocked to her affairs; invitations to her home were sought after. The nine years of their marriage were happy ones. When her husband saw that Nellie was becoming bored with the empty round of social life, he took her abroad and they retraced the steps she had taken on her famous trip.

Then tragedy struck. Seamon died very suddenly and Nellie's life was left empty again.

Once she had recovered from the shock of his death, Nellie found herself the possessor of a large fortune— over a million dollars—and the owner of her late husband's factory. There were offers to buy her out but she refused, partly because she was by now convinced that she had a clever business sense, and partly because her own vigorous, energetic self demanded something more to do than merely to sit around and spend money.

Nellie's confidence stemmed partly from the fact that she had never learned what it was to lose. She had always won; she expected to win.

It wasn't long before she found that running a business, a highly complicated, technical business, was far more complex than going out on her own to get a story. The factory made steel barrels, tanks, cans and tubes. The process of manufacturing and selling them, the handling of employees, the conferences with highly specialized engineers, the problems of bookkeeping, contracts, subcontracts, orders, inventories—all of this was a completely foreign world to her. She plunged in headlong, and soon found herself over her head and unable to swim in these strange waters.

There was no one to help her. Her ignorance was resented. Her efforts to take control were interpreted as meddling.

Worse yet, there were plenty to take advantage of her mistakes. While her own errors in judgment were having their results in the loss of huge sums of money to the company, at the same time unscrupulous employees were robbing her blind. The company's bookkeeping was "doctored" in such a way that company money was embezzled. When she discovered it she sued for recovery of the money, but so cleverly had it been done that the employee sued *her* for mismanagement! There were other disputes, other lawsuits. Customers and her own stockholders brought suits against her. She became involved in court litigations that lasted a long time—almost twenty years. Instead of the name "Nellie Bly" appearing in newspapers, now it was Mrs. Robert Seamon and her court battles that made news.

She lost every penny, even the factory, and finally went bankrupt. When she tried to form another company, she lost that, too, and creditors threatened her on every side.

In her terrible distress, not knowing which way to turn or whom she could trust, alone as she had never been alone before, she fled to Austria with what was left of her property and assets—assets which the courts claimed were not even hers. While she was there World War I broke out. Since she was in enemy territory, an Austrian business acquaintance persuaded her to transfer the stock and certificates to him for safekeeping.

This little transaction ended once and for all her illusions that she still had wealth. That wealth, what was left of it, had been strictly on paper, representing nothing but figures in dispute. But as long as she had the papers in her hands, she could fool herself. On her return to America, however, she found herself in trouble with the United States government, under the Alien Custodians Act, for having transferred property to the enemy. The transfer was not recognized, but the stocks were gone.

These years had been bitter, unhappy ones. They could not help but have their effect on Nellie. Always sensitive and proud, she now became more withdrawn and suspicious. She had almost no friends. She even quarreled with her brother who had offered to help her run the business.

Once before, when she had been penniless and alone, she had fought for a newspaper job and had fought her way to the top. But she had been young then and full of confidence in herself. Now once again she had to turn to newspaper work. But the mainspring of her arrogant sureness was broken. She wanted a job—not to prove to herself and the whole world that she could write just as well, that she could get stories no one else could—this time she wanted a job just so she could live.

In her distress, she turned to Arthur Brisbane. This outstanding editor of the New York *Journal* had been on the *World* staff with her. He knew her capabilities and didn't hesitate to give her a place on the *Journal*.

Once again stories appeared under her by-line. But they were no longer the old Nellie Bly stories.

She found herself in a different world from the one she had left so many years ago. This was the twentieth century. Styles in newspaper writing had changed. A new sophistication had come in; readers wanted a fast, racy, clipped kind of news reporting; they could no longer become aroused and indignant over the same things that had shocked an older generation. There had been so many Edward Phelpses since then that no newspaper would give the columns of space, day after day, that the *World* had once given her story. In an age where women were supposed to be equal and equipped to take care of themselves, no one was much alarmed at human wolves in Central Park.

Something else had changed, too, and for this she was directly responsible. Women reporters had come into their own. She was only one of many on the *Journal* staff. Girls were rapidly opening the doors for themselves to newspaper departments; they were writing society columns, initiating Women's Pages, becoming crack reporters, covering murder trials, fires, city hall—racing to get their stories on exactly the same terms as men. There was still not equality. Newspaperwomen were still not given the same status, the better jobs, the bigger pay-checks, as did the men, on the majority of newspapers. They still had to be exceptionally good to hold their own with just the average, run-of-the-mill male reporter. But they were making steady progress.

Nellie had pioneered this. There was not a woman reporter in the world who did not owe her a debt of gratitude. Out of curiosity, out of awe and out of deep respect, the feminine members of the *Journal* staff would have liked to become friends of hers.

But a habit of a lifetime had now become too deeply ingrained. She was unable to change with the times. Nellie was still a good writer. She knew her trade and she earned her pay. But the world she moved in had narrowed down to only a few interests: her two rooms at the Hotel McAlpin, her private office at the *Journal,* her work and her small, personal crusades for the rights of workingwomen and for a home for abandoned children. Even with these last two, she made no big splash about them. Unobtrusively, she found lost and homeless waifs and took them into her own two rooms until she could find shelter and care for them.

Out of her embittered years in the world of business, out of a sense of deep mortification in finding herself— once the toast and star of the nation's reporters—now a has-been, Nellie kept completely to herself. She made no friends.

Still a small woman, though no longer quite so slight or so slender, she still clung somewhat to the style of the clothes worn half a century earlier. Her skirts were long, her hands gloved, her hats always swathed in long, dark veils that hid her face from the scrutiny of her fellow workers.

Each morning she made her quiet way through the streets of New York—streets that had changed so much since she had been twenty years old and had first set foot in them. Now she threaded her way past automobiles, past trucks, past pedestrians who rushed by in a way that would have been undignified in 1887. The horses that had drawn the trolleys and the big wagons were gone. The hansom cabs were gone. There were as many women on the streets as men, and these women were so different from those she had known! These days, there was nothing unusual about a woman working in any profession or trade! Their faces painted, their skirts shorter, their motions and manners, so free and easy, their professional and business goals so much easier to achieve—Nellie could feel no kinship with them. She had no envy either, although sometimes she begrudged them their easier way.

Each morning she reported for work at the *Journal*. As she made her quiet way to her own office, she could not know that she was a figure of mystery to the others. But she did know—and this pained her—that she was not given the top stories, not sent out on the big assignments. To herself and to the others, she seemed out of date, out of place, out of the mainstream of the important newspaper life of the *Journal*.

But there was still to be one last big, dramatic story for Nellie Bly.

One day in 1920, Brisbane called her into his office. He was accustomed to her old-fashioned dress; in fact, he secretly admired her for her nonconformity to fashion.

Yet he was unable to repress a slight smile of amusement at the ceremony she made of removing her gloves, throwing back her veil and settling herself in the chair opposite his desk. He was so used to having his office door flung open by a careless hand, to having even his desk used as a chair by the new wisecracking, short-skirted flappers who were his women reporters.

"Nellie," he plunged right in, to cover both the amusement and also the worry he felt over the assignment he was to offer her, "there's a story—but you might not want to do it. The other women have been begging me for it, but I don't want to send out a kid on a thing like this. I'd be criticized—plenty. As it is, it's not the usual thing for a woman. You've been doing all the stories up till now—or most of them—on this Gordon Hamby murder trial. He seems to trust you."

"He sent me his Ouija board," she said. "And a note." She hunted in her large, shabby purse for it. "This is what he wrote: 'A slight remembrance (all I have at this time) for your infinite kindness and friendship.' He knew I was sympathetic—not for his crime, but for his youth. It seems so unnecessarily severe to execute a boy like that."

Brisbane nodded. "Well, because of your sticking so long to the case, and because of his liking for you, we have permission for you to be one of the reporters who will witness the execution. You will be the first woman to be at an execution in twenty-nine years in this state. What do you think?"

Her first impulse was to refuse, emphatically. She recoiled in horror at the very thought of watching something so barbaric to her—the state killing in punishment for a crime. It was not that she condoned the crime of murder; Gordon Hamby *had* killed. Society had a right to protect itself from him, but Nellie's own feelings were that society had no right to take his life in revenge.

That was her first thought. Her second was that of a newspaperwoman: to be the first woman in twenty-nine years to go beyond that little green door in the death house at Sing Sing! To be able to write an eye-witness account! And at last, after so many years of plugging away at unimportant stories, to have a really big one handed to her on a platter! She could not refuse.

"Will the authorities agree to my going?"

"They know how you feel about capital punishment. And there are strong, organized forces in this state who are actively campaigning against the extreme penalty. We have represented you as one of the leading people in this campaign (which in your own individual way you are), and the authorities were afraid to refuse the request. If they refused you, they might get politically attacked and they want to stay out of politics."

Nellie went to Auburn, New York, where the big prison of Sing Sing was located, with such a sinking feeling in her heart that she wondered if she could actually go through with it. Would she get sick? she worried. Disgrace herself and her paper? There were even moments, as she introduced herself to the warden, showed him her credentials and noticed the shocked, contemptuous look in his face, when she came close to hating both the *Journal* for sending her there and herself for being there. It was as close as she ever came to wishing she had never been a newspaperwoman.

In the death chamber she sat far to the back.

After it was all over she walked out with the rest, her back straight, her veil over her face concealing her emotions. Somehow she managed to make her way, without faltering, to her hotel room and to her desk. She was grateful for only one thing. This time she did not have to struggle with the stubborn keys of the typewriter that she had to use in her *Journal* office. Here, once again, she could write as she used to, with an easy-flowing pen and paper.

The shock, the pain, the anguish she had felt poured out in her story. She wrote:

### HORRIBLE! HORRIBLE! HORRIBLE!

Hamby is dead. The law has been carried out—presumably the law is satisfied.

Thou Shalt Not Kill. Was that Commandment meant alone for Hamby? Or did it mean all of us?

I only know that I kept repeating "Thou Shalt Not Kill! Thou Shalt Not Kill! . . . The horribleness of life and death. Through my mind flitted the thought that one time this young boy going to the death chair had been welcomed by some fond mother. He had been a babe loved and cherished. And this is the end. . . .

Though it was more an editorial against capital punishment than a story of the execution, Brisbane played it up prominently in the *Journal*. As in the past, when Nellie wrote with passion and feeling, from her own heart, she had the gift of being able to stir her readers.

This was Nellie Bly's last big story.

She was past fifty now, tired and ill. More and more

as she sat in her quiet little office at the *Journal,* the door firmly closed against the rackety hubbub of the city room outside, her thoughts would drift to the past. Instead of that office she would see the editor's office of the Pittsburgh *Dispatch,* with Madden seated at his old roll-top desk and herself so young, so torn between fright and daring, conscious of her hair about to come down over her shoulders and of her ill-fitting clothes. Or it would be Cockerill's office. It would be Pulitzer's face and she would feel her heart once more squeezed with the miracle of his faith in giving her her chance. She would see herself once again strong and young and confident, brimming over with ideas, hurrying up and down stairs, poking her nose into strangers' homes, into alleys, into factories and shops. She felt again the splash of ice-cold water the matron had thrown over her shivering self at Blackwell's Island.

It was all gone. Madden was dead. Pulitzer, the great idol of her life, was dead, too. And she? She was a legend, a living legend. She was aware that new reporters on the *Journal* peeked through doors to watch her pass in the corridors, that they were told in whispers of the once-great Nellie Bly, of her blaze of glory.

The trouble with legends was that they belonged to the past. She had outlived herself. And she had no wish to go on living.

Two years after the Hamby story, in 1922, Nellie Bly passed away.

So many other spectacular events had happened since her famous trip around the world that her own paper, the *Journal,* did not publicize this in the story it wrote about her. The *World* remembering her as the brightest

[ 184 ]

star in their whole firmament of reporters, did better. They gave her half a column of space, recalling her world-famous trip, her Blackwell's Island story and many others. There were notices about her in other papers, too.

There were tributes to her that would never get into print, living tributes—the reforms she had helped to start, the evils she had helped to change, the democracy she had worked so hard to strengthen and keep alive.

But the tribute that would have meant the most to her, if she could have read it, was a small one in the *Journal*. It meant that she had proved that she done what she had claimed she could do on that long-past day in the office of the Pittsburgh *Dispatch*. In that tribute it said:

". . . she was considered the best reporter in America."

# Bibliography

## GENERAL

BARRETT, JAMES WYMAN. *The End of The World*. New York: Harper and Bros., 1931

BARRETT, JAMES WYMAN. *The World, The Flesh, and Messrs. Pulitzer*. New York: The Vanguard Press, 1931

BLEYER, WILLARD GROSVENOR. *Main Currents in the History of American Journalism*. Boston, Mass.: Houghton, Mifflin Co., 1927

HUDSON, FREDERICK. *Journalism in the United States from 1690 to 1872*. New York: Harper and Brothers, 1873

HUGHES, HELEN MACGILL. *News and the Human Interest Story*. Chicago: University of Chicago Press, 1940

LYNCH, DENIS TILDEN. *Boss Tweed*. New York: Boni and Liveright, 1927

ROSS, ISHBEL. *Ladies of the Press*. New York: Harper and Brothers, 1936

SEITZ, DON CARLOS. *Joseph Pulitzer, His Life and Letters*. New York: Simon and Schuster, 1924

SWETNAM, GEORGE. *Pittsylvania County*. New York: Duell, Sloan and Pearce, 1951

VAN WYCK, FREDERICK. *Recollections of An Old New Yorker*. New York: Liveright, Inc., 1932

VERNE, JULES. *The Omnibus Jules Verne*. New York: J. B. Lippincott and Co.

WALKER, STANLEY. *City Editor*. New York: Frederick A Stokes Co., 1934

WALTZ, GEORGE H. *Jules Verne*. New York: Henry Holt and Co., 1943

WILLARD, FRANCES ELIZABETH. *American Women*. New York, Chicago: Mast, Crowell and Kirkpatrick, 1897

[ 186 ]

## BOOKS BY NELLIE BLY

COCHRANE, ELIZABETH. *Nellie Bly's Book: Around the World in Seventy-two Days.* New York: The Pictorial Weeklies Co., 1890

——. *Six Months in Mexico.* New York: J. W. Lovell Co., 1888

——. *Ten Days in a Mad-house or Nellie Bly's Experience on Blackwell's Island.* New York: N. L. Munro, 1887

## MAGAZINES AND NEWSPAPERS

RITTENHOUSE, MIGNON. "They Called her the Amazing Nellie Bly." *Good Housekeeping Magazine,* February, 1955. Pages 48 to 51.

*The World.* Bound copies and microfilms, 1885 through 1895: New York Public Library.

# Index

[ 191 ]

[ 192 ]